CW00377243

Guideline no. 66

Guidelines for the design and safety of food microbiology laboratories

Second edition

Prepared by the QA QC Working Party of the Microbiology Panel

2011

© Campden BRI 2011
ISBN: 978 0 907503 68 2

Station Road, Chipping Campden, Gloucestershire, GL55 6LD, UK
Tel: +44(0)1386 842000 Fax: +44(0)1386 842100

www.campden.co.uk

SCOPE

This document covers design concepts and safety requirements needed for UK based food microbiology laboratories up to and including Containment Level 2. Industry best practice and guidance on legal requirements is covered.

OBJECTIVES

This document provides a point of reference for the design and safety of food microbiology laboratories. It should facilitate the identification of key considerations relating to the essential details of legislation, and recommended/best practice design requirements when considering any of the following:

- A new build

- Review and updating existing facilities

- Moving to a different facility

- Decommissioning

LIMITATIONS

This document only covers laboratories up to Containment Level 2 as defined by the Advisory Committee for Dangerous Pathogens.

Except where there is a particular safety aspect, the document does not cover operational management such as equipment operating procedures, methods and bench practices. This is covered by Campden BRI Guideline 9 - "A Code of Practice for Microbiology Laboratories Handling Food, Drink and Associated Samples". From now on this document will be referred to as Guideline 9.

It does not cover the project management of the building work for a microbiology laboratory itself, but will highlight the special requirements for such a laboratory and provide the necessary reference points.

Aspects of design and safety, which are not specific to food microbiology laboratories, are not covered, e.g. General Building Regulations and Health and Safety at Work Act 1974.

This document does not cover requirements for any Post Mortem facility, which must be physically separated from the microbiology laboratory. Further information on PM facilities is available from:

- Health Services Advisory Committee (2003). *Safe working and the prevention of infection in clinical laboratories and similar facilities* (2nd edition). ISBN 0 7176 2513 3

- NHS Estates (2005*). Facilities for mortuary and post mortem rooms.* Health Building Note 20. 3rd edition.

- Health Service Advisory Committee (2003). *Safe Working and the Prevention of Infection in the Mortuary and Post Mortem Room.* 2nd edition. ISBN 0 7176 2293 2

- Department of Health (2006). *Health Technical Memorandum 07-01 - Safe Management of Healthcare Waste.* Available as a download *http://www.dh.gov.uk/dr_consum_dh/groups/dh_ digitalassets/documents/digitalasset/dh_073328.pdf*

- HSE (2000) *Common Zoonoses in Agriculture.* Available as a download *http://www.hse.gov.uk/pubns/ais2.pdf*

- Advisory Committee on Dangerous Pathogens (2003) *Infection at work: Controlling the risks* Available as a download *http://www.hse.gov.uk/pubns/infection.pdf*

Throughout this document a number of web links to external websites are given. These were correct at the time of writing but are not future proof.

This edition covers much of the current existing legislation but the readers must satisfy themselves that this has not been superseded and is still applicable. It is the responsibility of the laboratory management to ensure that it complies with current safety regulations.

Members of the Working Party for the second edition

Miss Fiona Brookes (Chairperson)	Northern Foods plc
Mrs. Alison Atkinson	Weetabix
Dr. Clive Blackburn	Unilever Colworth
Mrs. Bridgette Clarke	Bakkavor
Mrs. Jane Duddle	Waitrose
Dr. Adrianne Klijn	Nestlé (UK) Ltd.
Mrs. Jan McClure	Unilever
Ms. Karen Sims	Tesco Stores Ltd.
Mrs. Rian van der Doelen	Masterfoods
Mr. Andy Walker	Premier Foods Group

Campden BRI

Dr. Chris L. Baylis

Mrs. Sarah Ealey

Mr. Mike Jeffries

Dr. Suzanne Jordan (Technical Secretary)

Miss Christina Oscroft

Miss Ann Wood

CONTENTS

1. INTRODUCTION

There are strict legal obligations for microbiology laboratories to ensure that they are designed to comply with certain safety criteria and that they are operated in accordance with safe practice. This is required in order to contain the microorganisms and minimise the risk of cross contamination to personnel and other test samples both within and outside the laboratory.

This document is intended to give advice on the requirements of the laboratory environment, equipment and personnel practices in order to achieve the above. Additionally, there is information on a logical approach to design and construction to assist logical workflows and to aid efficiency, which in turn will lead to safe working practices.

1.1 Application

This document is applicable whether designing a new facility, modifying an existing one, or reviewing current standards in use.

All sections are equally relevant in each of the above scenarios.

For new builds, the key considerations are given to achieve the required standards and these should be integral from the design concept stages through to project management of the completed facility.

Modifications to existing facilities may vary from major extensions to the facility or layout changes to improve work flows, increase throughput or accommodate new equipment. Conversely, the modification may be to downsize the facility. In all cases, this document can be used as a reference to identify the key elements required to both maintain the previous standards and to ensure that new legislation is incorporated into the revised facility.

It is also important to carry out scheduled reviews of existing facilities, where new legislation and actions taken to previous issues encountered may both have a bearing on the current suitability of that facility with regards to operation and health and safety.

In all instances the legal considerations for the construction and design of laboratories are very important. The legal requirements for general building will apply, such as those relating to fire protection, escape routes, electricity regulations, water bye laws etc. With microbiology laboratories, however, there are specific regulations for containment and handling infectious material which must be adhered to. This is referred to in greater detail in Section 2.

2.   LEGAL REQUIREMENTS

It is essential that information on the legal requirements related to the construction and operation of a food microbiology laboratory is obtained. This mainly concerns the required containment for pathogens. Even the simplest food microbiology laboratory will be handling pathogens as defined legally. For example, most Enterobacteriaceae and Coliforms are considered to be Group 2 pathogens, and a few such as *E. coli* O157 are considered to be Group 3 pathogens.

Further details on containment requirements are given in Section 2.1.3. A list of relevant literature is given in the reference section.

2.1   Laboratory design and construction

2.1.1 Building regulations

Compliance with the relevant Building Regulations is essential. Professional help must be sought because not only are there national regulations but there are also local restrictions which must be followed.

The legislative framework of the 'Building Regulations' is principally made up of:

• The Building Regulations 2000; and

• The Building (Approved Inspectors etc.) Regulations 2000

Both have been amended several times since 2000, the most recent time on 8 September 2009.

The latest amendments in 2009 were delivered through:

1   The Building and Approved Inspectors (Amendment No. 2) Regulations 2009 (SI 2009/2465)

2   The Building (Amendment No. 2) Regulations 2009 (SI 2009/2397)

3   The Building and Approved Inspectors (Amendment) Regulations 2009 (SI 2009/1219)

4   The Building (Amendment) Regulations 2009 (SI 2009/466)

The Building Regulations actually consist of a number of separate booklets known as approved documents, generally referred to as Parts. Each Part is given a letter and in England and Wales these run from Part A (which deals with structure) to Part P (which deals with electrics).

They can be downloaded freely from the 'Professional User' section of the Planning Portal website. *www.planningportal.gov.uk.*

Scotland and Northern Ireland have their own similar building regulations, but sections have been allocated different letters. The Republic of Ireland uses the same part letters as those for England and Wales.

The Planning Portal website: *www.planningportal.gov.uk* contains all the latest information and includes charges, which increase regularly. Each local council has a building control department that employs building inspectors who assess plans and visit sites to ensure that the plans are adhered to during construction.

The Building Regulations are continually being updated. Many builders do not keep up to date with these and rely on their designers to have satisfied the Regulations in their drawings and for the building inspector to put them right if the situation on site demands it.

There are other regulations governing building alteration and construction. Links can be found through the Planning Portal website.

2.1.2 Construction regulations

In addition to the Planning and Building Regulations issues there are Health and Safety considerations with both new builds and adaptations of existing facilities. The Construction (Design and Management) Regulations 2007 (CDM 2007 SI 2007 No 320) came into force in July 2007.

http://www.opsi.gov.uk/si/si2007/pdf/uksi_20070320_en.pdf

These Regulations are intended to focus attention on planning and management throughout construction projects, from design concept onwards. The aim is for health and safety considerations to be treated as an essential, but normal, part of a project's development - not an afterthought or bolt-on extra. They replace the Construction (Design and Management) Regulations 1994 (CDM94) and the Construction (Health, Safety and Welfare) Regulations 1996 (CHSW). There is an Approved Code of Practice (ACOP) that replaces the previous (1994) ACOP. It provides practical guidance on complying with the duties set out in the Regulations.

http://www.hse.gov.uk/pubns/priced/l144.pdf

Guidance given to CDM co-ordinators and principal contractors in this ACOP gives an indication as to what is needed, but any action taken should be in proportion to the risk which the work creates. The architect, lead designer or contractor who is carrying out the bulk of the design work should normally co-ordinate the health and safety aspects of the design work; the builder or main contractor, if there is one, should normally co-ordinate construction work.

The ACOP states that it is vital that those doing the work understand the risks involved and what to do about them. If the risks are low and the precautions well understood by those carrying out the work, then there will be no need for a written plan. In other simple cases a brief summary that clearly sets out who does what and in what order will be enough. Where the risks are higher, which for laboratory construction may include structural alterations, unusual safeguards (e.g. pathogen destruction prior to laboratory closure or demolition) and heavy lifting operations (e.g. autoclaves), then more detailed planning, assessment and documentation may be required.

Additionally, when constructing or altering a laboratory the facilities must be designed to ensure compliance with the requirements of the Workplace (Health, Safety and Welfare) Regulations 1992 (SI 1992 No 3004).

http://www.hse.gov.uk/pubns/priced/l24.pdf

This regulation consolidates other pieces of legislation relating to workplaces and welfare facilities and employers have a duty to ensure that workplaces under their control comply with these regulations. Owners and landlords who have control over workplaces or communal areas also have this duty. The regulation is split into 27 regulations each with a specific focus, although the first four encompass citation and commencement, requirements, application and interpretation.

Regulation 5 concerns maintenance of workplaces and equipment that contributes to the workplace. The Approved Code of Practice (ACOP) and guidance requires suitable maintenance systems comprising checks, tests, remedial action and records for emergency lighting, fencing, ventilation systems etc.

Regulation 6 concerns the requirement for suitable ventilation and the need for a failure warning device if mechanical ventilation is used. The ACOP recommends that the fresh air rate should not fall below five to eight litres per second for each occupant and that the ventilation should not cause uncomfortable draughts.

Regulation 7 concerns temperature. A maximum temperature is not specified but the temperature must be 'reasonable' with the avoidance of excessive effects from sunlight. A minimum temperature of 16°C is required, unless severe physical work is being undertaken in which case 13°C is sufficient.

Regulation 8 concerns lighting. Natural light is preferred, with the requirement that windows and skylight should be regularly cleaned. All lighting must be sufficient and suitable for purpose. Emergency lighting powered by an energy source independent of the normal artificial lighting is required in areas where there would be a danger if the artificial lighting failed.

Regulation 9 concerns cleanliness and waste materials. The work environment must be of a design that enables it to be cleaned and it must be kept clean. Waste must not be allowed to accumulate and must be stored in appropriate containers. The operational correct disposal of waste falls under the Environmental Protection Act 1990.

Regulation 10 concerns Room Dimensions and Space. The ACOP recommends $11m^3$ of open floor space for each person, using a room height of 3m for this calculation.

Regulation 11 concerns workstations and seating, although specific requirements for workstations with visual display units are subject to the Health and Safety (Display Screen Equipment) Regulations 1992 (SI 1992 No 2792).
http://www.opsi.gov.uk/si/si1992/uksi_19922792_en_1.htm

The link to the ACOP for this regulation is: *http://www.hse.gov.uk/pubns/priced/l26.pdf*

The remaining regulatory sections of the Workplace (Health, Safety and Welfare) Regulations concern floors, traffic routes, falls, falling objects, windows, skylights, doors, gates, washrooms, drinking water, rest and changing facilities etc.

It is also advisable to read some of the information on sick building syndrome. Poor building design can contribute to headaches, respiratory irritation, fatigue, discomfort and illness. Some of the features identified by the World Health Organisation which contribute to sick building syndrome include poor forced ventilation, poor lighting, glare, low relative humidity, release of chemical vapours, excessively warm environment and airtight (windows not opened) rooms (Sykes, 1989).

Many of the above features will be encountered in a microbiology laboratory. Most microbiology laboratories will therefore require controlled ventilation, controlled temperature, daylight or adequate illumination and air extraction for noxious vapours. The Workplace (Health, Safety and Welfare) Regulations cover this in general, but more specific requirements for microbiology laboratories are laid down in "The management, design and operation of microbiological containment laboratories". This covers the latest guidance from The Advisory Committee on Dangerous Pathogens and gives detailed technical information on the design, management and operation of containment laboratories.

The guidance expands and explains the legal requirements set out in the biological agents provisions of COSHH, with particular attention to how these requirements influence design, construction and operation of laboratories. It covers health and safety management in microbiological containment laboratories, the general principles of the design and operation of microbiological containment laboratories and the principal requirements for Containment Level 2 and 3 laboratories.

All food testing laboratories require Containment Level 2 and a few, such as those testing for VTEC, may require Containment Level 3. More details of Hazard Groups and Containment Level requirements are given in Section 2.1.4.

2.1.3 Fire regulations

Suitable fire exits, alarms, extinguishers etc. must be provided. There are often additional local bye-laws governing fire prevention and the local Fire Prevention Officer should be consulted for advice on provision of fire exits, alarms and emergency lighting. Fire safety begins with the design and construction of a building. Any amendments to existing buildings must also be designed to meet the requirements of fire safety. The fire safety requirements are controlled by the Building Regulations 2000 (SI 2000 No 2531) which require appropriate fire safety measures to be incorporated in the build of new or altered premises. This will include suitable means of warning and escape, fire resistance of materials and the construction to prevent the spread of fire. There are often additional local bye-laws governing fire prevention and the local Fire Prevention Officer should be consulted for advice on provision of fire exits, alarms and emergency lighting. Building construction (e.g. walls, doors, ceiling voids, windows) will be influenced by fire prevention considerations and it is therefore very important that plans are approved by the local Building Control Officer before construction commences.

The Regulatory Reform (Fire Safety) Order 2005 (SI 2005 No 1541) is the primary piece of fire safety law in the workplace. This had lead to a change in the focus of the requirements for compliance from a prescriptive format to a risk assessment based approach to ensure that the construction and fire safety provisions are relevant and appropriate for the facility. Advice on carrying out such risk assessments is given in "A short guide to making your premises safe from fire".

http://www.communities.gov.uk/documents/fire/pdf/144647.pdf

The Dangerous Substances and Explosive Atmospheres Regulations 2002 (DSEAR) require that risks from the indoor storage of such substances is controlled by elimination or by reduction of quantities stored to a minimum. Laboratories frequently store such substances, e.g. flammable liquids, such as industrial methylated spirits. When not in use, containers of flammable liquids must be kept closed and stored in suitable containers of fire-resistant construction and which are designed to retain spills (110% of the volume of the largest vessel stored). These should be located in designated areas away from the immediate work area and not compromise escape routes. The quantity of liquid held in the immediate work area for active use should be minimised and not be more than that required for one work shift. There must be mitigation provided to protect against foreseeable incidents.

There are two useful ACOP's relevant to DSEAR:

Dangerous Substances and Explosive Atmospheres   *http://www.hse.gov.uk/pubns/priced/l138.pdf*

Storage of Dangerous Substances *http://www.hse.gov.uk/pubns/priced/l135.pdf*

Insurance companies should also be consulted to check that fire prevention measures are considered adequate. Some insurance companies may demand additional measures to be in place for protection of data.

2.1.4 Microbiology containment

The term "containment" describes the way in which microbiological agents are managed in the laboratory environment to prevent and control the exposure of laboratory workers, other people and the outside environment to the agents in question. Microbiological agents are included in the general Control of Substances Hazardous to Health (COSHH) regulations, with more detail available in Schedule 3 of the Regulations. COSHH classifies biological agents into one of four Hazard Groups (HG) based on the following criteria:

> Whether the agent is pathogenic for humans
> Whether the agent is a hazard to employees
> Whether the agent is transmissible to the community
> Whether there is effective treatment or prophylaxis available

Microorganisms are classified into four hazard groups (HG) defined as follows

Hazard Group 1   An organism that is unlikely to cause human disease.

Hazard Group 2   An organism that can cause human disease and may be a hazard to employees; it is unlikely to spread to the community and there is usually effective prophylaxis or treatment available.

Hazard Group 3   An organism that can cause severe human disease and may be a serious hazard to employees; it may spread to the community, but there is usually effective prophylaxis or treatment available.

Hazard Group 4   An organism that causes severe human disease and is a serious hazard to employees; it is likely to spread to the community and there is usually no effective prophylaxis or treatment available.

In allocating agents to a hazard group, no account is taken of particular effects on those whose susceptibility to infection may be affected, for example, because of pre-existing disease, medication, compromised immunity, pregnancy or breast feeding. Any additional risks to such employees should be considered as part of the general risk assessment.

The Advisory Committee for Dangerous Pathogens (ACDP) has been responsible for publishing the classification of biological agents in the Approved List of Biological Agents. This classification is reviewed and updated periodically and is available on the HSE website *www.hse.gov.uk/pubns/misc208.pdf.*

This should be consulted to ensure that the most up-to-date version is in use. Below, however, is a list of microorganisms that are most likely to be encountered in a standard food laboratory.

Biological agent	Classification
Actinomycis spp.	2
Bacillus cereus	2
Campylobacter jejuni	2
Campylobacter spp.	2
Clostridium botulinum	2
Clostridium perfringens	2
Clostridium spp.	2
Enterobacter aerogenes/cloacae	2
Enterobacter spp.	2
Enterococcus spp.	2
Escherichia coli (with the exception of non-pathogenic strains)	2
Escherichia coli (Verocytotoxin-producing strains e.g. *E. coli* O157: H7)	3
Klebsiella pneumoniae	2
Klebsiella spp.	2
Listeria monocytogenes	2
Listeria spp.	2
Proteus mirabilis	2
Pseudomonas aeruginosa	2
Salmonella arizonae	2
Salmonella Enteritidis	2
Salmonella (other serovars)	2
Salmonella paratyphi A, B, C	3
Salmonella typhi	3
Shigella dysenteriae (Type 1)	3
Shigella dysenteriae (other than Type 1)	2
Shigella flexneri	2
Shigella sonnei	2
Staphylococcus aureus	2
Vibrio cholerae (including El Tor)	2
Vibrio parahaemolyticus	2
Vibrio spp.	2
Yersinia enterocolitica	2
Yersinia spp.	2

Laboratories working with biological agents belonging to HG 2 need to work to Containment Level (CL) 2; laboratories working with biological agents belonging to HG 3 need to work to CL3. Although there are no legal containment requirements under COSHH for laboratories working with HG 1 biological agents, the practices, safety equipment and facilities are essentially similar to those that are required at HG 2. Furthermore, preliminary isolation of bacteria may unintentionally propagate biological agents that belong to HG2, therefore a food microbiology laboratory must be constructed to at least CL2.

The main pieces of guidance for the food microbiology laboratory are as follows:

1   Biological Agents: Managing the Risks in the Laboratory and Healthcare Premises: *http://www.hse.gov.uk/biosafety/biologagents.pdf*

2   Infection at Work: Controlling the Risks: *http://www.hse.gov.uk/pubns/infection.pdf*

3   The Management, Design and Operation of Microbiological Containment: Laboratories: (HSE Books ISBN: 9780717620340)

4   Infection Risks to New and Expectant Mothers in the Workplace: A Guide for Employers (HSE Books ISBN 9780717613601)

There are some minimum standards legally required for CL2, CL3 and CL4 laboratories handling HG2, HG3 or HG4 agents respectively. These are given in Table 1 overleaf.

Note: Where there are human patients or animals that are, or are suspected of being, infected with a HG3 or HG4 biological agent, the most appropriate control and containment measures from this table should be selected with a view to adequately controlling the risk.

Table 1   COSHH containment measures for the laboratory, animal room or industrial processes
(Extracted from "Biological Agents: Managing the Risks in Laboratories and Healthcare Premises")

	Containment Level		
	2	3	4
Air handling			
The workplace is to be maintained at air pressure negative to atmosphere	No	Yes	Yes
Input air and extract air to the workplace are to be filtered using high efficiency particulate absorption (HEPA) filters or equivalent	No	Yes, on extract air	Yes, on input and double on extract air
Security and access			
The workplace is to be separated from any other activities in the same building	No	Yes	Yes
Access is to be restricted to authorised persons only	Yes	Yes	Yes, via air-lock key procedure
Efficient vector control, e.g. rodents and insects	Yes, for animal containment	Yes, for animal containment	Yes
Safe storage of a biological agent	Yes	Yes	Yes, secure storage
An observation window, or alternative, is to be present, so that occupants can be seen	No	Yes	Yes
Disinfection and disposal procedures			
The workplace is to be sealable to permit disinfection	No	Yes	Yes
Specified disinfection procedure	Yes	Yes	Yes
Surface impervious to water and easy to clean	Yes, for bench	Yes, for bench and floor (and walls for animal containment)	Yes, for bench, floor, walls and ceiling
Surfaces resistant to acids, alkalis, solvents, disinfectants	Yes, for bench	Yes, for bench and floor (and walls for animal containment)	Yes, for bench, floor, walls and ceiling
Incinerator for the disposal of animal carcasses	Accessible	Accessible	Yes, on site
Protective equipment and procedures			
Infected material, including any animal, is to be handled in a safety cabinet or isolator or other suitable equipment	Yes, where aerosol produced	Yes, where aerosol produced	Yes

Additional guidance and best practice is detailed in "The Management, Design and Operation of Microbiological Containment: Laboratories" (2001 HSE Books).

The HSE must be notified when a laboratory premises uses organisms from Hazard Group 2 or above for the first time. This therefore applies to new laboratories and relocated laboratories. Notification forms are available from the HSE website. Further supporting guidance on when to notify is available on the HSE website.

https://www.hse.gov.uk/forms/notification/cba1notes.htm.

Further security measures are required when working with certain organisms that are listed in the Antiterrorism, Crime and Security Act (2001). Part 7 contains the information relevant to the storage and pathogens and toxins listed in Schedule 5. This was further updated with Statutory Instrument 929 (2007), which now includes *Clostridium perfringens.* All laboratories intending to use organisms listed on Schedule 5 should contact their local Counter Terrorism Security Advisor (CTSA). Additional information and contact details are available on the NATSCO website: *http://www.nactso.gov.uk/pathogens.php*

2.1.5 Other regulations

When considering what precautions are necessary to control risks associated with a project, everyone who has a duty must take account of the general principles of prevention specified in Schedule 1 to the Management of Health and Safety at Work Regulations 1999 ('the Management Regulations').

http://www.hse.gov.uk/pubns/priced/l21.pdf

Other regulations that need consideration include:

The Electricity at Work Regulations 1989 (SI1989 No 635). Advice on the Electricity at Work Regulations (1989) is available from the Health and Safety Executive, who also have information guides to the Pressure Systems and Transportable Gas Container Regulations (1989).

2.2   Operational health and safety

2.2.1 Health and Safety at Work Act and Management of Health and Safety at Work Regulations

The Health and Safety Act at Work Act (1974) and the Management of Health and Safety at Work Regulations (1999) set out the general responsibilities in a legal framework; they are aimed to protect people and the public from risks which may arise from work activities. These responsibilities cover the main parties such as employer and employee, but also include other parties such as contractors and visitors. Failure to comply with either the general requirements of the Act or specific requirements may result in legal proceedings.

Employers have the responsibility to ensure, as far as is reasonably practicable, the health, safety and welfare at work of all their employees. To carry out a duty "so far as is reasonably practicable" means that the degree of risk in a particular activity or environment can be balanced against the time, trouble, cost and physical difficulty of taking measures to avoid the risk.

The Act specifies an employer's general duty, such as ensuring that the place where their employees work is in a safe condition and does not pose a risk to health. This includes ways into and out of work such as staircases that need to be well lit, and passages and roadways that need to be kept clear from obstacles. Employers must provide and maintain machinery, equipment and other plant to ensure that these are safe and without risk to health. The working environment itself, which covers heating, lighting, ventilation and noise, must be considered to safeguard the health and safety of the employees. Employers must provide adequate arrangements for the welfare at work of their employees; this covers facilities such as seating, washing arrangements and toilets.

Employers must ensure that all their employees are competent to carry out their jobs in a safe manner, minimising the risk to themselves and others. They must provide information, instruction, training and supervision. Articles and substances at work that may compromise employees' health and safety, for example machinery and chemicals, are also controlled by law. It is not only the duty of the employer, but also of manufacturers and suppliers of materials, to ensure that these materials are safe and present minimal risk to health, so far as is reasonably practicable. Users must be given sufficient information about the use and any hazards associated with the material. Employers have a duty to ensure that employees are not put at risk by contact with the material, including during handling and storage.

The Act also specifies the employees' duties. All employees must take reasonable care for the health and safety of themselves and of other persons who may be affected by what they do or fail to do at work. This implies not only avoiding obvious silly or reckless behaviour, but also taking positive steps to understand the hazards in the workplace and to comply with safety rules and procedures.

Reference: L1 A Guide to the Health and Safety at Work Act 1974.

2.2.2 Health and safety management

There are six key elements to successful health and safety management. These are policy, organisation, planning and implementing, measuring performance, reviewing performance and auditing.

The employer has a duty to prepare and keep up-to-date a health and safety policy. If there are more than five employees the policy needs to be in writing. The policy should reflect how the employer is controlling risks and has to be communicated to the employees. The second element is organising: this ensures that the health and safety policy is put into effective practice. The goal is to create a positive culture with participation on all levels. Recognised Trade Unions have the right to appoint safety representatives to represent the employees in consultations with the employer about health and safety matters. Employers must consult with safety representatives; if requested by two or more safety representatives, a safety committee should be established.

There needs to be a systematic approach to policy implementation. Careful planning will ensure a coordinated effort from all people involved. In the planning stage it is important that responsibilities are assigned and performance standards and objectives are set with an appropriate time scale.

Measuring performance is an essential aspect of maintaining and improving health and safety performance, as it will indicate when action is needed to improve standards. Performance can be measured actively (monitoring the achievement of plans and the extent of compliance with standards) and reactively (monitoring accidents, ill health and incidents).

Reviewing performance and auditing provides a feedback loop that will enable organisations to maintain and develop their health and safety management systems. Performance can reviewed by analysing data, monitoring activities and auditing the whole health and safety management system. More information on the health and safety management can be found in HSG65. *Reference: HS (G) 65.*

Under the Management of Health and Safety at Work regulations employers are required to set up emergency procedures for dealing with serious and imminent danger and for danger areas. Employers need to appoint competent persons to ensure compliance with identified arrangements, to devise control strategies as appropriate and to limit access to areas of risk to ensure that only those persons with adequate health and safety knowledge and instructions are admitted. Employers must also ensure that, where necessary, contacts are made with external services, such as first aid, emergency medical care and rescue work.

The responsibilities for employees are not as onerous as for employers, but effective health and safety does require their complete involvement. In practice that means taking reasonable care; this requirement is expressed in both criminal and civil law. Employees are expected to take an active part in preventing accidents; they must use any equipment, material or substance provided to them in accordance with any training and instruction. Within the limits of their training and instruction, every employee shall inform their employer (e.g. via supervisory staff) of any (a) situation that represents a serious and immediate danger or (b) shortcoming in the employer's protection arrangements. Employees must take reasonable care of their own health and safety and that of others who may be affected by their acts and omissions. Employees should not interfere with, or misuse, anything provided to secure health and safety - e.g. remove first aid equipment.

2.2.3 Risk assessments

Under the Management of Health and Safety at Work Regulations employers have to carry out assessments of (a) the risks to health and safety of their employees to which they are exposed at work; and (b) the risks to the health and safety of persons not in their employment arising out of, or in connection with, the conduct by them of their undertaking.

When risk assessments are required it is important that employers ensure that adequate steps are implemented to prevent or control exposure to the hazards identified. Prevention could be the substitution of a hazardous substance by an alternative non hazardous material. e.g. the quality control of certain media can be carried out using less pathogenic or non-toxigenic strains. Where substitution is not possible, the employer must apply protection measures appropriate to the activity and consistent with the risk assessment. The selection of control measures for biological agents should take into account the fact that there are no exposure limits for them. Their ability to replicate and to infect at very small doses means that exposure may have to be reduced to levels that are at the limit of detection.

Where adequate control of exposure cannot be achieved by other means, in addition to the previous measures, the provision of suitable personal protection equipment (PPE) such as protective clothing, protective gloves, footwear and eye protection may be required. In assessing whether the use of PPE is the appropriate option, employers should consider the limitations and costs of PPE, the practical difficulties of ensuring its correct use, its effectiveness in the actual work situation and the type and level of exposure to the hazardous substance concerned.

Risk assessments have to be reviewed regularly or if there is reason to suspect that the risk assessment is no longer valid, or if there has been a significant change in the work to which the risk assessment relates, or if the results of any monitoring that has been carried out indicate it to be necessary. Details of the risk assessment process are outlined in section 6.11.

In addition to the general risk assessments, specific risk assessments have to be done in respect of young persons and new or expectant mothers. Refer to section 6.11 for further details of the risk assessment for these specific groups.

2.2.4 Control of Substances Hazardous to Health COSHH 2002

The Control of Substances Hazardous to Health Regulation was updated in 2002 and applies to a wide range of substances including individual chemical substances or preparations such as paints, cleaning material, metals, pesticides, insecticides and biological agents. Biological agents are defined as a microorganism (a microbiological entity, cellular or non-cellular, which is capable of replication or of transferring genetic material, e.g. bacteria, fungi and viruses), cell culture, or human endoparasite, whether or not genetically modified, which may cause infection, allergy, toxicity or otherwise create a hazard to human health. The substances hazardous to health can occur in many forms, e.g. solids, liquids, vapours, gases, dusts fibres, fumes, mist, aerosols and smoke; the form taken by a substance can be a contributory factor for its potential harm. There are several routes by which hazardous substances may enter the body. They include ingestion, inhalation (local and systematic effects), injection or when the substance comes into contact with the skin where they can cause dermatitis or are absorbed through the skin. Under COSHH, employers have a duty to carry out COSHH risk assessments; this is necessary to assess if the work that is carried out will expose employees to substances that are hazardous to health and to ensure that adequate steps are implemented to prevent or control exposure to these substances. Additional details of COSHH risk assessments for biological agents and chemicals are outlined in section 6.10.

2.2.5 Reporting of Injuries, Disease and Dangerous Occurrences Regulations (RIDDOR 1995)

Under the Reporting of Injuries, Diseases and Dangerous Occurrences Regulations (RIDDOR 1995) there is a legal requirement to report work-related deaths, major injuries (and diseases) and over-three day injuries sustained by people at work as well as certain dangerous incidents (near miss accidents) to the relevant authority (HSE/EHO).

- Major injuries include:
  - any fracture, other than the finger, thumbs or toes
  - dislocation of the shoulder, hip, knee or spine
  - chemical or hot metal burn to the eye or any penetrating injury to the eye
  - acute illness due to exposure to biological agents or their toxins

- Over-three-day injuries
  - Not classified as major
  - Caused by a work related accident that results in injured employee / self-employed person working on the premises being off work for more than 3 days or unable to carry out their normal range of duties for more than 3 consecutive days

- Diseases include:

  - conditions due to physical agents and the physicals demands of work (e.g. carpal tunnel syndrome)
  - conditions due to chemical and other substances (e.g. ethylene oxide poisoning)
  - infections due to biological agent (e.g. anthrax and legionellosis)

- Dangerous occurrences include:

  - failure of any load bearing part of any lift or hoist
  - failure of any pressurised closed vessel in which the internal pressure was above or below atmospheric pressure, where the failure has the potential to cause the death of any person.
  - accidental release of any substance which may damage health

Infections must only be reported when notified in writing by a doctor that the employee is suffering from one of the infections listed in RIDDOR that is linked to the corresponding activity. Infections that are common in the community and cause diarrhoea and colds are therefore not reportable. However, where there is reasonable circumstantial evidence, e.g. known contact with the infectious agent in laboratory work, then a report should be made. Dangerous occurrences, in other words incidents which could have resulted in the release of a biological agent that could cause severe human disease, must also be reported. This would include diseases caused by HG3 micro-organisms such as *E. coli* O157:H7.

Reference: A guide to the Reporting of Injuries, Diseases and Dangerous Occurrences Regulations 1995.

2.2.6 Waste disposal

Waste should be categorised as to whether it is 'non-hazardous' waste that can be disposed through normal waste routes (e.g. food samples, paper and packing) or 'hazardous' waste (e.g. microbiological waste and chemical waste) that requires specific safe disposal procedures.

The legislation for waste disposal is constantly changing depending on the environmental issues prevailing at the time. The laboratory should ensure that all waste is rendered safe before it leaves the control of the laboratory, or that competent contractors who have the facilities to handle laboratory waste are used.

There are several regulations covering the disposal of hazardous biological waste including:

Control of Substances Hazardous to Health (COSHH) Regulations 2002
Hazardous Waste (England and Wales) Regulations 2005
Collection and Disposal of Waste Regulations. SI 1988 no. 819, ISBN 9780110868196
Environmental Protection Act 1990
The Waste Management (England and Wales) Regulations. Statutory Instrument 2006 No. 937

Materials covered under the category of "clinical waste" include animal bedding, hospital waste, sharps, pharmaceutical products, drugs, dressings, radioactive waste, chemical waste, human and animal tissues or body fluids and infectious waste. The Collection and Disposal of Waste Regulations (1988) also refer to clinical waste as waste that may cause infection to persons coming into contact with it. Advice on disposal of clinical waste is provided by the HSE (2003).

Although most food laboratories do not handle genetically modified organisms, there are additional regulations. Disposal of genetically modified organisms and the waste products thereof is covered by the Genetically Modified Organisms (Contained Use) Regulations, 2000 and section 108 (1) (a) of the Environmental Protection Act 1990.

2.2.6.1 Microbiological waste disposal

Decontamination in the laboratory usually means autoclaving for the required time/temperature to render the waste material safe. Autoclaves (and associated services) should be large enough to cope with the anticipated workload of the laboratory. Alternatively, contaminated waste may be collected in sealed containers by a specialist contractor who has appropriate high temperature incineration facilities.

Some local authorities require that waste from a microbiology laboratory should be handled in the same way as clinical waste. The main criteria governing clinical waste disposal are firstly safety (is waste rendered safe before disposal) and secondly aesthetics (syringes, dressings, body tissues may be autoclaved but their appearance may still be visually offensive) or they may constitute a physical hazard that would not be safe for landfill disposal. Generally, food microbiology laboratory waste can be autoclaved and rendered microbiologically safe and in most cases the plastic disposables melt down and are unrecognisable afterwards. As such this material does not appear to come under the definition of clinical waste. If the laboratory handles animal waste (e.g. raw chicken carcasses) then it is almost certain that incineration of the waste will be required. On-site incineration is not recommended because of cost and complexity of regulations governing this activity. It is better to use an outside specialist company.

However, laboratory sharps (e.g. syringe needles, scalpel blades) should be classified as clinical waste. Special containers will be required for their transport and final disposal must include incineration.

For waste that can be autoclaved, suitable autoclave cycles need to be determined dependent on the type of waste and the volume of liquid waste. For example, maximum volumes need to be established for fluid cycles to ensure that the material is adequately sterilised. Codes of practice should be prepared by competent staff to cover the contained storage of waste prior to collection and autoclaving. The frequency of collection from the laboratory should be included as well as procedures to follow in the event of autoclave failure (e.g. storage of contaminated waste over a weekend in closed containers).

2.2.6.2 Chemical waste disposal

The disposal route for chemical waste will be dependent upon whether it is hazardous or non hazardous. Non-hazardous liquid waste can generally be flushed to waste with copious amounts of water down the laboratory sink. Examples of non hazardous waste include dilute disinfectant solutions, pH buffer solutions and very dilute acid and alkali solutions. Prior to disposal down the sink the relevant manufacturer's safety related documentation should always be consulted.

Historically, disposal of hazardous chemical waste from laboratories was principally done by flushing down the drain with water. This is no longer acceptable.

The principal legislation to be followed is the Environmental Protection Act 1990, which sets up the requirements for Waste Disposal Authorities. In addition to the separate treatment of microbiological and/or clinical waste, it is necessary to segregate chemical waste into a number of classes, both because the disposal methods employed by the contractor will be different depending on the type of material involved, and also because chemical reactions may be initiated by mixing certain materials.

As with microbiological waste, an outside specialist company will have to be used for chemical waste and their advice should always be sought. The specialist contractor should have a range of waste disposal options that include high temperature incineration, chemical treatment, recycling/reclamation, landfill disposal or dilution and subsequent treatment as trade effluent. It is essential to minimise the risk to the specialist contract staff and so it is vital that codes of practice are rigidly observed and a technically competent member of staff takes responsibility for the disposal. This includes preparation of hazard waste disposal notes containing sufficient detail to accurately describe the waste.

Chemical waste that is contaminated with microorganisms, but unsuitable for autoclaving, must be segregated into the chemical categories described above and placed in a sealable, single use bin (as described in 2.5.1) for disposal by the specialist contractor.

References:
Info from HSE website: Department of Health (2006). Health Technical Memorandum 07-01: Safe Management of Healthcare Waste.

http://www.dh.gov.uk/dr_consum_dh/groups/dh_digitalassets/documents/digitalasset/dh_073328.pdf

3. DESIGN AND OPERATING SPECIFICATIONS

Construction of a microbiology laboratory from conception to completion generally follows a set of stages as follows:

i. Appointment of project team. This will normally include the laboratory manager, a senior manager with budget responsibility, a member of the health and safety team, and a site engineer.

ii. Evaluation of options and constraints by the project team, i.e. the most cost effective solutions such as modification of an existing building, a completely new structure or portable building. During the design process the following points should be considered:

   • Type and volume of work
   • Environmental impact
   • Security
   • Relevant legal standards
   • Other activities being carried out in the vicinity
   • Future expansion and/or change of use

   During the evaluation process it may be necessary to take expert advice from structural engineers, architects or designers.

iii. Production of concept drawings, based on the estimated costs and requirements of the project team. This will include floor plans and services, based on advice available in this manual. The input of a professional designer or architect may be useful if this type of expertise is not available in house.

iv. Presentation of concept drawings to senior management may be required to ensure that the project remains within overall financial approval. The presentation should therefore be detailed, since cost may be the most important aspect examined, and may need some of the legal justification and support suggested by this manual.

v. Feedback by senior management on the interim presentation/concept drawings.

   Production of the necessary detailed drawings (including any necessary amendments) by the architect/design team for submission to the local planning office for examination by the various departments of Safety, Fire and Environmental Health.

vi. Permission to proceed having been granted, a further review of the project should be made to establish time scales and their effect on the continuing business, before final authorisation is granted by senior management.

vii. Submission of formal planning application and approval by the planners.

   Final go-ahead granted, there should be further intermediate reviews as construction proceeds with the seal of approval from the Fire/Safety/Security Officer before occupation and use.

Figure 3.1 Flow diagram of laboratory design and construction

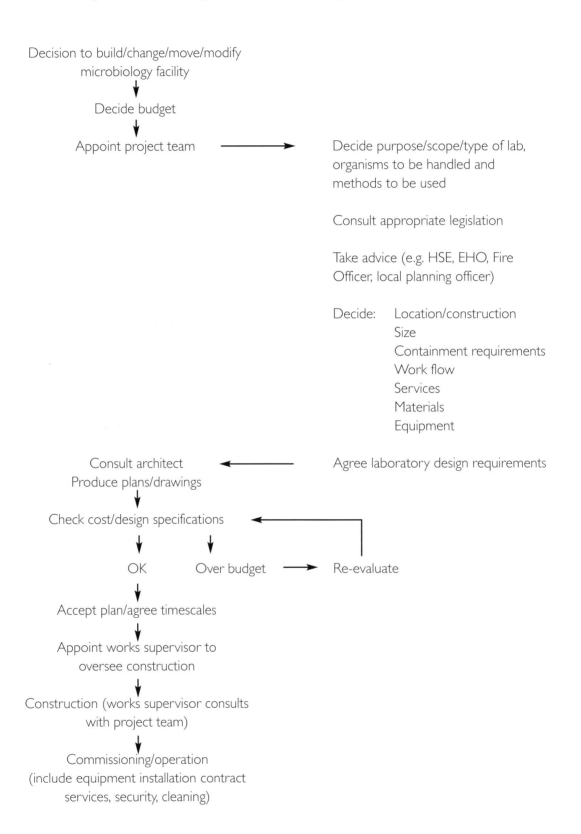

3.1   Siting of laboratory

The laboratory should be a dedicated facility in a building of sound construction, preferably situated in a single storey building or the ground floor of a multi-storey building. There should be good access for deliveries of bulky materials and equipment. It must be separate from production areas and should be separated from the chemistry laboratory. Where the latter is not feasible, microbiology and chemistry safety, containment and hygiene rules apply to the whole laboratory.

If it is not possible to have a separate building, care must be taken to ensure that air outlets and drainage systems do not affect or connect with food production areas. Remember that a building previously used for a different purpose will not necessarily meet the requirements for use as a laboratory. New or altered buildings should comply with the relevant building and fire regulations.

3.2   General requirements

Provision should be made for:

- An entrance/exit vestibule for changing and hand washing
- Receipt of samples
- Access for large pieces of equipment
- Writing up/office area separate from the laboratory working area
- Media preparation and storage
- Sample preparation and incubation
- Subculturing of samples
- Handling reference cultures
- Autoclaving
- Washing up
- Storage of waste awaiting disposal
- Storage for samples separate from other materials
- Handling and storage of laboratory coats

Each of these items might require its own room in a large laboratory complex, whereas several might be combined in one room in a smaller facility.

3.3   Size of laboratory

This will be site specific and dependent on the current and anticipated methods, volume and nature of work. Adequate space must be allowed for unimpeded workflow. In general, 24 m^3 per person is a minimum guideline. Space will be required for incubators, refrigerators, media, consumables etc. and this should be calculated as being additional to the working laboratory area. Service access is necessary for autoclaves and other equipment, so allowance should be made when siting these items. There are also minimum requirements for the space that must be left between benches or equipment; the recommended figures given in BS3202 (Laboratory furniture and fittings) are.

i.	one worker, no traffic	975mm	-	1200mm
ii.	one worker, plus passageway	1050mm	-	1350mm
iii.	passageway only	900mm	-	1500mm
iv.	two workers back to back with no traffic	1350mm	-	1950mm
v.	two workers back to back plus passageway	1650mm	-	1950mm

3.4   Security and access

The laboratory should be designed such that access can be restricted to authorised personnel. Visitors, including service engineers etc., should not be able enter the laboratory area without a member of the laboratory staff being present. Guideline No. 9 deals with some of these aspects, especially access for cleaning staff.

3.4.1 Access for large equipment

The main entrance to the laboratory suite and at least one door to each separate laboratory should be a minimum of one and a half standard door widths. Where there is lift access, dimensions and load limits should be commensurate with the largest, heaviest piece of equipment anticipated to require access. This is usually an autoclave.

Ideally, access should not necessitate carrying equipment up or down stairs, round very tight corners in corridors, or through factory production areas.

3.5   Workflow and design

A logical pattern of workflow will determine the arrangement and segregation of areas. Basic principles that should be followed are:

i. The laboratory must be designed to prevent access by unauthorised persons.

ii. Writing/office areas should be separate from the laboratory working area.

iii. There should be a clearly defined sample receipt and logging-in area.

iv. Samples should follow a defined path through the laboratory, namely sample preparation/ weighing out, incubation, examination of cultures, and autoclaving of contaminated materials to washing up. Segregation of these activities in terms of separate rooms would be ideal, but a minimum of two rooms should suffice for a small laboratory. These would comprise a media/wash up area and a laboratory. The media/wash up room should have an autoclave and/or this room can be connected to the laboratory by a double-entry autoclave.

v. There should be adequate storage facilities, see section 3.5.1 - Storage requirements.

3.5.1 Storage requirements

Adequate space should be made available for the following:

i. General stores of a size and location to allow easy access, effective stock control and good housekeeping practices.

ii. Flammable solvents. Storage of flammable solvents is covered by the Highly Flammable Liquids Regulations 1974. Bulk outside storage must be in locked metal bins or in a locked brick store approved by the Fire Officer. **NB**: the store may need to be licensed. The Methylated Spirits Regulations (1987) also requires certain solvents to be kept in a locked cupboard. The maximum total volume that can be stored in each laboratory is 50 litres. This must be stored in a safety container within a flammable solvents cupboard, sited away from sources of heat. Spark-proof refrigerators are required for storage of solvents and solvent-based solutions. The solvent store may also fall within the scope of the Dangerous Substances Explosive Atmosphere Regulations 2002 (DSEAR). If this is the case then additional precautions will have to be taken.

iii. Refrigerators and freezers. Separate refrigerator and freezer space should be provided for chemicals, samples, microbiological cultures and prepared media.

iv. Records. Adequate separate and secure storage space must be provided for records. Ideally this store should be fire-proof. Some accreditation schemes require records to be maintained for no longer than 6 years. Generally, day-to-day laboratory records should be maintained for at least two years. Software and disk records may also be stored in this area.

Reference: The Dangerous Substances and Explosive Atmospheres Regulations 2002.

3.5.2 Laundry

An adequate supply of clean laboratory coats must be available. Some laboratories may decide to install their own laundry facilities, in which case the requirements for hot water, drainage, drying and ironing of the coats should be considered at the design stage.

3.5.3 Computers

Advice should be sought from the computer manufacturer or the company's Information Technology Department as to whether the operation of a computer or storage of computer discs/tapes in a particular laboratory environment could pose a hazard. Particular care should be taken to avoid damage due to chemical, microbiological or dust contamination, heat, damp and magnetic fields.

Suitable secure storage will be fireproof, flood resistant and shielded from strong magnetic and electric fields.

3.6   Ventilation and temperature control

Environmental control must be provided for personnel comfort and equipment control. This can be achieved in a variety of ways, but full consideration must be given to the heat generated in the laboratory and the effect of any resultant air turbulence on equipment. A temperature range of 16-22°C is generally satisfactory for laboratory work. Areas where high humidity is expected, e.g. media preparation and autoclave rooms, may require additional ventilation and/or air extraction.

For comfortable working conditions, air velocity should not exceed 0.15m/s in winter and 0.25m/s in summer. Note that safety cabinets, laminar flow cabinets and balances may be adversely affected by excessive or turbulent airflow in the laboratory.

Where mechanical ventilation/air conditioning is used, it should be designed to take account of heat load and other equipment that may affect its operation. Other extraction systems, e.g. extraction fans, fume cupboards and safety cabinets, may unbalance the ventilation system, and increase the requirement for supply of air into the laboratory. Action may be required to boost the supply of air that should either be 100% fresh air or partially recycled. It is preferable to keep a slight under pressure in the laboratory. Input air systems need only be dust filtered. Extracted air from the laboratory must not vent near factory doors or windows or air intakes, or into factory production areas.

Temperature control may be achieved by wall, ceiling or floor mounted air conditioning units. These will require connection to an external heat exchanger unit. Sizing of the units should take account of the heat load generated by both laboratory activities and equipment. Air conditioning units often require a condensate drain.

Dust containment or extraction (portable recirculatory units are available) is recommended for weighing of powdered media or samples to minimise laboratory contamination and to protect laboratory workers (in particular asthmatics).

Experts in the field should be consulted.

References:
HSE (2000). General ventilation in the workplace. Guidance for employers. Health and Safety Executive, ISBN 9780717617937.
BS 5925 (1991 Confirmed 2007). Code of practice for ventilation principles and designing for natural ventilation. ISBN 0 580 19285 7.
Building Regulations (2000), F: Ventilation (2006).

3.7 Personal amenities

3.7.1 Hand washing and coat changing

Hand washing facilities must be provided at the entrance/exit to the microbiology laboratories and at the entrance to each individual laboratory. Non-hand operated taps are preferable. The size and precise arrangements will depend on the number of staff. The layout must be designed to guide personnel into the correct coat change procedure, e.g. hands must always be washed after removing the laboratory coat and before handling factory or outer clothing. There must be separate pegs or hangers for laboratory coats so that they do not come in contact with non-laboratory clothing. Laboratory coats must not be worn outside the laboratory and factory coats must not be worn in the laboratory.

3.7.2 First aid

The First Aid at Work Code of Practice (1997) and the Health and Safety (First Aid) Regulations (1981) gives guidance on the provision of first aid facilities. First aid boxes and sealed containers of sterile water or 0.9% saline for eye washing should be provided. These should be situated in a convenient clean location. The Code of Practice also gives advice on the extent and location of first aid facilities, which may include the provision of a first aid room. There should be an adequate supply of clean cool water to allow for a 10 to 15 minute rinse of chemical burns. Other facilities, such as an emergency shower, should be considered in relation to the anticipated risks. First aid supplies should be checked regularly to ensure that they are within date and replacements can be ordered where necessary.

3.7.3 Canteen facilities

Staff should have ready access to a canteen or snack bar/break room separated from the laboratory facilities. Provision of a refrigerator in the canteen will prevent staff from being tempted to store food or drink in the laboratory. Eating or drinking must not be allowed in any laboratory area.

3.7.4 Toilet facilities

These should be sited outside the laboratory to ensure correct coat removal and hand wash procedures.

3.8 Noise control

The 2005 Noise at Work Regulations place responsibility on employers to keep noise to the lowest levels 'reasonably practicable'. Generally, high levels of noise are not associated with microbiology laboratories; however, autoclaves, pumps, laminar air flow/safety cabinets, air conditioning units and ultra-sonic baths can generate a lot of noise. The level at which it is recommended that ear protectors are worn is 85 decibels; however, they must be supplied and worn at >90 decibels. It is unlikely that levels in a microbiology unit would approach these figures. Refer also to a HSE document Noise at Work (2005) and HSG 56 Noise Guides 3 to 8 (2005). Where possible, noisy equipment should be sited so that any noise nuisance can be minimised. Alternatively, silencing systems and/or insulation should be provided. Reference should also be made to the relevant sections of the Building Regulations (2001), E Resistance to the passage of sound.

3.9 Fire fighting equipment

Carbon dioxide extinguishers and fire blankets are the most appropriate for laboratories. Advice must be sought from the local fire prevention officer and insurance company on numbers and location of fire fighting equipment.

4. CONSTRUCTION DETAILS

4.1 Construction, fitments and surface finishes

4.1.1 The building (See also 3.1, siting of laboratory)

Any sound building may be suitable. A laboratory may be in a purpose-built block, or adapted from an existing building. Portable buildings may be suitable (see section 8), but will present special difficulties. Consider with caution, and get expert advice (see section 3.3 - size of laboratory). Routine access to the laboratory should be through an entrance hall or vestibule (see also section 3.4 - security and access that includes considerations for access for large equipment).

References: Building Regulations (2000), A: Structure (2006)
Building Regulations (2000), M: Access and use of buildings (2006)

4.1.2 Walls

Walls need to be smooth, cleanable and impervious to water and chemicals. Recommended types are food factory finishes, including plastic panels, and sprayed or brushed paints. Tiles may be used, but unsealed wood should be avoided. Choose light or neutral coloured, non-reflecting finishes which do not interfere with reading of tests. Note that white may cause glare.

Where partitioning is used, mount on coved plinths at least 10cm high, sealed to the floor to facilitate cleaning. Also note that shelves or equipment mounted on partitioning may need racking for support. Where the laboratory is converted from an existing area, re-route electrical and plumbing services where possible to avoid the laboratory, or construct sealed boxing to avoid trapping dirt.

4.1.3 Floors

Floors need to be able to withstand the conditions likely to be found, for example, heat, water, vibration. Pay special attention to loading, as some equipment is heavy (see Building Regulations, 2000). Floor finishes should be impervious to water and chemicals and non-slip where necessary. All laboratory floors must be sealed to the wall junction by coving up the wall to a minimum height of 10cm. Recommended types include sheet safety flooring, and painted or trowelled finishes. Specialist advice should be obtained. Tiles and wood should be avoided.

4.1.4 Ceilings

A room height of 2.5m is adequate for ceilings. The finish should be smooth and cleanable. For suspended ceilings, to keep the laboratory airspace completely separate, ensure that the roof void is partitioned and sealed off from adjoining voids.

4.1.5 Light fittings

Light fittings tend to attract dirt and dust. These should be enclosed but accessible for cleaning and maintenance. Domestic strip lights with diffusers are adequate.

4.1.6 Lighting

Artificial daylight tubes are recommended and advice is available from commercial suppliers (see also Section 4.1.5 - Light fittings). It is recommended that a minimum of 750 lux is provided at bench level. Localised 1200 lux lighting on work benches may be required for specialist tasks. Emergency lighting is required for safety purposes in the event of power failure (see Section 4.2.1.4 - Emergency electrical supplies).

4.1.7 Decor

Use light, non-intrusive colours, and avoid shiny surfaces. A working microbiology laboratory should be subject to the minimum of disturbance. Therefore the use of low-maintenance finishes, for example scrubbable wall paints and metal or plastic window frames, is helpful.

4.1.8 Doors

The number of doors must be adequate to meet the fire regulations (ref. Building Regulations 2000B: Fire Safety). At least one route into the laboratory should have doors of one and a half standard widths to allow passage for large equipment. Doors need to be robust. They may be made from painted or varnished wood, plastic or metal. Glazed vision panels should be fitted to access doors and self-closing devices should be fitted to entrance doors.

References:
Building Regulations (2000), N: Glazing - materials and protection (2006).
Advisory Committee on Dangerous Pathogens (2001).

4.1.9 Windows

Windows should be non-opening and sized and positioned to make use of natural light. If possible, double glazed sealed units should be fitted to avoid condensation. Plastic or metal frames are preferable. Sloping window sills will avoid a build up of clutter and dust. If windows are south-facing, use solar reflecting glass or protective film. Exterior blinds or canopies may be helpful, but internal blinds or curtains should not be used unless enclosed within double-glazing. The Building Regulations Approved Document L1B 2006: conservation of fuel and power will govern the type of windows that can be installed in the laboratory in order to improve energy efficiency. This document also applies to insulation and heating as well as ventilation and lighting systems.

4.1.10 Benches

Bench layout should maximise usable working space and provide access for cleaning. U- or L-shaped layouts may be unavoidable in small rooms, but may give less useable space in corners and result in awkward joints in the bench tops. The preferred height is 850-950mm. The height and depth of equipment to be sited under the worktop should be taken into account. Most laboratory benching is 750mm deep as standard, although wider benching may be required to take account of size of equipment. Allow 150mm behind for services. Knee-holes should be about 600mm wide. Refer to Section 3.3 (Size of laboratory) for spacing requirements. Bench legs must be cleanable, so metal is preferable, but sealed wood may be used to support bench tops. Metal bench frames must be earthed.

4.1.11 Work tops

These should be level, smooth, scratch-resistant, and impervious to water and chemicals, and must be able to be disinfected. Use laboratory grade laminates, stainless steel, or coved solid polymer board with a minimum 7cm high upstand at the wall junction. Tiles should be avoided and wood should not be used on surfaces, but may be part of the infrastructure. Joints should be kept to a minimum. Hard polymer sheet should be pre-machined with holes for taps. Consider some non-fixed benches to allow flexibility for later alteration.

Reference: Advisory Committee on Dangerous Pathogens (2001)

4.1.12 Service outlets

Mounting outlets for gas, air, pure water and other services, either on the wall or above the bench, avoids clutter and reduces dirt traps on the bench surface. Electrical sockets are particularly difficult to keep clean, and are vulnerable to splashes (see also Section 4.2, Services).

4.1.13 Cupboards

Cupboards should be robust to withstand usage (BS3202, 1991). Inaccessible dead spaces around cupboards should be avoided by adequate design to facilitate cleaning. Surfaces must be cleanable, and a laminated finish is advised. The handles should be easily cleaned and designed not to trap dirt. Cupboards should be mounted on castors, or sealed to the floor by coving, or cantilevered fittings should be used to clear the floor to avoid trapping dirt beneath. Fixed cupboards reduce flexibility.

4.1.14 Shelving and wall cupboards

These need to be strong and well-fixed and easily accessible. Avoid installation above bench tops, where staff might have to reach over cultures, and where heat sources may cause fires.

4.1.15 Sinks

A large sturdy stainless sink and drainer are essential in the preparation area. A double sink/double drainer may be needed where there is no glass-washing machine. Fit large taps to give adequate flow. Inset sinks tend to be inadequate for the preparation area, but can be useful elsewhere, particularly for staining slides. Swan-necked taps with screw-on spigot outlets are particularly adaptable for other uses. Stainless steel sinks must be earthed.

4.1.16 Hand-wash basins

A hand-wash facility must be sited near the exit (Advisory Committee on Dangerous Pathogens, 2001) and preferably in each room where cultures are handled. Taps should be non-hand operated, for example, wrist or elbow levers, foot, knee, or sensor operated. Space should be allowed for bactericidal soap and disposable towel dispensers and waste collection. Stainless steel hand-wash basins must be earthed.

4.1.17 Seating

Some tasks in the laboratory will require seating for staff, e.g. microscopy, plate counting. Any seating provided should be adjustable for safety and comfort and readily cleanable.

Reference: HSE Seating at Work (1991).

4.2   Services

Service layouts should be planned to allow as much flexibility as possible. Maintenance and modifications will be required and the layout should allow for this with the minimum of disturbance.

Service pipes, outlets and stop taps should be colour coded for easy identification:

Water	Green
Steam	Grey
Compressed air	Blue
Gas	Yellow

Reference: BS 1710 - Identification of Pipelines and Services, 1984.

4.2.1 Electricity

Electrical installations must comply with "The Electricity at Work Regulations 1989". Installation and maintenance should be carried out by a competent and qualified electrician.

4.2.1.1 Loading
The electrical supply system must be sufficient to cater for the maximum usage required. It is always advisable to over-estimate, as requirements usually increase with time. Any requirements for 3-phase supply should be identified as early as possible and the electrical contractor informed.

4.2.1.2 Socket outlets and power connections
Sufficient 13 amp switched socket outlets, connected to ring circuits or spurs, should be provided to allow all portable appliances likely to be used simultaneously to be individually supplied. It is recommended that all power outlets are protected by residual current circuit breakers (RCCB) within the laboratory with the exception of controlled temperature storage units.

Trailing flexes are a hazard and must be avoided. Power points should not be located where they are at risk from water or steam.

Appliances up to 13 amps can be connected to the standard supply. These should be provided with individual on/off switches.

It is recommended that fixed appliances and equipment are permanently connected wherever possible. Appliances rated above 13 amps and those requiring 3-phase supply must be permanently connected to dedicated switched isolators.

Electrical equipment is subject to portable appliance testing regulations unless directly connected to mains (hard wired) (HSE PM32, Plugs and Sockets Regulations, 1994).

4.2.1.3 Uninterruptable power supply (UPS)/Surge protection

Some computers and computer controlled equipment can be susceptible to variations in the power supply. Such equipment may require a UPS unit or surge protection. Equipment suppliers will advise.

4.2.1.4 Emergency electrical supplies

If power cuts are a potential problem, the provision of a back-up system should be considered (see also Section 4.2.5 Lighting).

4.2.1.5 Electricity distribution board

The electricity distribution board for the laboratory will often be shared with other areas within the building. Therefore, it is recommended that this board is not sited in the laboratory. Where practicable the distribution board should be located in a controlled access area. However, if it is to be sited in a general access area, then is should ideally be in a corridor.

4.2.1.6 Computer terminal requirements

Where computer terminals or individual personal computers are in use in a laboratory, splash-proof keyboards may be required. In laboratories handling significant quantities of powder, remote siting of disc drives and printers is also recommended.

4.2.1.7 Telephone points

Wall-mounted telephones are recommended for laboratories. In some areas instruments with a "hands-free" loud-speaking facility may be preferable.

4.2.2 Water systems

Water pipes must be earthed.

4.2.2.1 Cold water

i. Supply - A suitable cold water supply can be via mains (direct or stored) or borehole (direct or stored). This may be treated before use.

    Softened water may be required for some purposes, particularly if the main supply is from a hard water area (e.g. autoclaves and dishwashers).

    Reverse osmosis, distilled or deionised water will be required for media manufacture and for the final rinse after washing up.

    Where there is a risk of back feeding into the water supply it will be necessary to install a break-tank. A non-return valve on its own is not acceptable. Local water bye-laws must be complied with. See Bye-law No. 11, Type "A" air break as defined in the Water Supply Bye-laws Guide.

Consideration must be given to the water bye-laws (Water Supply (Water Fittings) Regulations 1999.) when configuring the cold water supplies within a building containing laboratories. In order to comply with the regulations, domestic (e.g. drinking fountains and machines, kitchens and toilets) cold water supply must be kept separate from the laboratory system.

ii. Pressure

    Where equipment requires a specific pressure to operate and it is considered that connecting to the pressurised mains constitutes a risk of back feeding, then either a boost pump or raising the height of the header tank should be considered.

iii. Flow rate

    Where equipment requires continuity of flow to fulfil its function, e.g. a still, consideration should be given to this at the design stage in sizing the main supply tank and pipe bore.

iv. Safety showers

    Safety showers, if fitted, must be provided with a guaranteed, independent water supply - this is usually a dedicated tank. No valves must be fitted between the supply and the shower. The supplier of the equipment will be able to advise on details of minimum amount of water required. Shower heads may require regular disinfection. The shower tank will need regular emptying and disinfection to comply with the *Legionella* regulations (refer to section 4.2.2.3 for details)

4.2.2.2 Hot water

On a factory site, the normal factory hot water supply will be satisfactory. However, hot water utilising factory recovered water (i.e. recovered from process) is not suitable and should not be used. In this case laboratory hot water should be generated independently, for example, by immersion heater, steam calorifier or multipoint heater. Supply must be sufficient and consistent.

Consideration must be given to the water bye-laws (Water Supply (Water Fittings) Regulations 1999) when configuring the hot water supplies within a building containing laboratories. In order to comply with the regulations, domestic (e.g. drinking fountains and machines, kitchens and toilets) hot water supply must be kept separate from the laboratory system.

4.2.2.3 Legionella regulations

The design and operation of the hot and cold water system must comply with the *Legionella* Regulations: see Prevention and Control of Legionellosis (1991), CIBSE TM13 (2002), BS 6700 and Control of Legionellosis (2001). Advice should be sought from a qualified engineer. The temperature of the cold water should be maintained as low as possible with **a maximum of 20°C**. Stored hot water must be held at >55°C except for large systems which must be >60°C.

4.2.2.4 Steam

Steam supply systems must comply with the requirements of the Pressure Systems and Transportable Gas Containers Regulations (Statutory Instrument No. 2169, 1989). The steam pressure must be compatible with the instruments it is used for and reducing valves may be necessary. Some boiler additives may cause problems, e.g. corrosion of autoclaves and stills and contamination of media). If in doubt, consult the equipment supplier.

4.2.3 Gas

4.2.3.1 Fuel gas

Gas installations should be carried out in accordance with the Gas Safety (Installation and Use) Regulations 1998, i.e. use CORGI registered contractors. Gas pipes must be earthed. Gas isolating valves should be fitted to individual rooms for safe isolation.

Safety gas taps should be fitted where supplying gas burners, e.g. Bunsen Burners. For safety reasons independent portable gas burners (e.g. Camping Gas) are not recommended. However, where their use is unavoidable care must be exercised.

4.2.3.2 Cylinder gases

Cylinder gas installation and supply must comply with the Pressure Systems and Transportable Gas Containers Regulations (Statutory Instrument No. 2169, 1989). Cylinders must always be transported and stored in an upright position and must be secured to a solid item to prevent them falling when in use. They must be kept cool (see Section 5.10 - Gas cylinders).

Consult gas and equipment suppliers for advice on specific applications.

Reference: (Pressure systems and transportable gas containers regulations, SI 1989 no. 2169, HSE Guide to Pressure Systems and Transportable Gas Containers Regulations 1989).

4.2.4 Compressed air

Compressed air supplies must be dry and oil free and must comply with the Pressure Systems and Transportable Gas Containers Regulations 1989. Refer also to HSE Compressed Air Safety (1998). A suitable supply pressure for laboratories is 15-20 psi unless specialist equipment requires higher pressures. Independent air lines, i.e. those not fitted to equipment, must be fitted with safety nozzles.

4.2.5 Drainage

See Building Regulations (2000) - H: Drainage and waste disposal. The drainage system should be designed to provide sufficient capacity to convey the maximum discharge without blockage and allow easy access for cleaning, inspection and maintenance. Present and any likely future requirements must be considered.

The effluent load in terms of the quantity and compositional quality must be established to ensure that site discharge consents are complied with. Advice should be obtained from the water company.

On factory sites, laboratory drains should be routed away from production areas. Where this is not possible, they must be routed so that a single unjointed drain of suitable material passes through production areas into a sealed drainage trap. Stainless steel (316), glass, polypropylene and other plastics may be suitable depending on type of effluent. Advice should be obtained.

Back siphonage must be prevented. Drains from sinks must be fitted with traps. Condensate drainage from air conditioning units should have air breaks and traps as defined in the DHSS HN (Hazard) 856, 9th July 1985 report.

Details of draining requirements for autoclaves are specified in BS2646, Part 2.

4.2.6 Ventilation (see also 3.6 - ventilation and temperature control)

Rooms in which a large amount of water vapour is produced should be ventilated by a fan-assisted extraction system. This can be a simple wall-mounted extractor fan or, where no external walls are present, a ducted system. The discharge point should have a fly-screen and be sited to allow rapid dissipation of vapour to atmosphere.

Ventilation ducting should be cleanable and there should be sufficient access for inspection, servicing and removal of filters. Extract fans are better positioned at the outlet end of extract ducting to maintain duct pressure at a negative pressure to its surroundings in case of leaks.

Laboratory ventilation or air conditioning ductwork must not connect to the factory system or other non-microbiology areas, e.g. offices or canteens. External discharge points for extracts should be protected against back pressure from wind and must be located to avoid reintroduction of exhausted air via intakes or windows.

Coarse pre-filter and 55m pore size dust filters must be fitted where there is any air intake as part of the system. Consider the implications of where this air will be drawn from. Filters must be easily accessible for inspection and maintenance.

References:
HSE 1990 Ventilation
HSE 1988 Guidance Note EH22

4.2.7 Vacuum

A piped vacuum system will not normally be required. Portable vacuum pumps supplying at minus 0.5 to minus 0.6 bar should be sufficient for most laboratory work.

4.2.8 Waste disposal

Waste chutes are **not appropriate** for microbiology laboratories. Sink mounted waste disposal units should be of catering or industrial grade to cope with laboratory waste.

5.   INSTALLATION AND SAFETY ASPECTS OF EQUIPMENT

General requirements for all equipment:

The laboratory should have available all necessary equipment to allow the correct conduct of testing activities and supporting operations. The equipment should be suitable for the required purposes and capable of achieving the required accuracy. After installation, equipment should be validated/checked before use and thereafter covered by appropriate calibration and/or monitoring checks and maintenance (see Campden BRI Guideline No. 9 for details).

Prior to purchasing any equipment the following should be considered with regard to choice and location of equipment:

- Required utilities (e.g. water, drainage, electricity, gas)

- Environmental conditions (e.g. temperature, humidity, vibration, noise)

- Equipment impact on surrounding environment (production of heat, noise, humidity, vibration, odour etc.)

- Equipment dimensions with respect to accessibility and siting (weight, and dimensions)

- Technical specifications (capacity, sensitivity, accuracy, precision etc.)

- Operational costs and considerations (on-going servicing, calibration and maintenance/repair requirements)

Many pieces of equipment will have a site installation guide available from the manufacturer.

In addition to the safety requirements of the equipment there are general requirements for the operation of electrical equipment. The HSE website *(http://www.hse.gov.uk/electricity/withequip.htm)* provides a good source of information on the installation and operation of electrical equipment and the work standards required.

5.1   Legislation

Prior to installation of any item of laboratory equipment the appropriate legislation must be consulted and considered.

This legislation includes:

- Management of Health and Safety at Work Regulations 1999

- The Electricity at Work Regulations 1989

- Personal Protective Equipment at Work (PPE) Regulations 1992

- Manual Handling Regulations 1992

- Provision and Use of Work Equipment Regulations 1992

- Health and Safety (Display Screen Equipment) Regulations 1992

Electrical equipment is subject to portable appliance testing regulations unless directly connected to mains (hard wired) (HSE PM32, Plugs and Sockets Regulations, 1994).

5.2   Anaerobic and Modified Atmosphere Generating Systems (MAGS)

Modified atmospheres, e.g. anaerobic/microaerophilic, can be provided by a modified atmosphere workstation (e.g. anaerobic workstation) for large-scale work; for many laboratories, the use of small sealable containers or jars with a gas generating pouches is more appropriate.

5.2.1 Anaerobic workstations

Installation

Large anaerobic equipment is supplied with a special atmosphere from gas cylinders (see Section 5.11: Cylinder gases and Section 4.2.3.2 - Cylinder gases). Provision needs to be made for piping the gas to the equipment. Ideally, gas cylinders should be stored outside the building in a secure tamper proof area and the gas piped through to the laboratory. However, in practice gas cylinders for anaerobic workstations are generally fastened securely to a firm fixture adjacent to the workstation. Cylinders must be correctly stored and secured at all times. Expert advice must be sought for all gas installations. This should include gas mixtures, regulators and the handling and installation of cylinders.

For workstations a power supply is also required.

Safety

Some gas mixtures are potentially explosive and flammable.

Regular training in the safe use of the workstation and cylinder handling is required.

Reference: HSE Guide to Pressure Systems and Transportable Gas Containers Regulations 2000.

5.2.2 Gas jars

Installation
No specific requirements.

Safety
Users of commercial gas generating systems (pouches) must ensure compatibility with the jar being used. Use of the wrong combination of pouch (type or gas volume) and jar can result in an explosion.

5.3 Autoclaves

The autoclave is used for sterilisation of media and of waste material prior to disposal. Separate autoclaves for media processing and waste disposal are preferred.

Installation
Advice on planning, installation and use can be found in BS 2646 that describes the importance of site location and access, floor loading, drainage, capacity, space requirements, ventilation, noise transmission and services required for installation of an autoclave. Some autoclaves may require 3-phase electricity supplies, steam, water and compressed air. Drainage needs to take account of autoclave discharge temperature and should not connect directly to food production areas. An air break should be incorporated in the drain to prevent back flow.

Electrical: A lock-off system is required. If 3-phase is required, the autoclave should have a switched and fused isolator within 1.5 metres.

Steam
Any steam supply line and vent pipes should be insulated to prevent burns to personnel. The supply line should be fitted with an industrial pressure gauge (Bourdon type) complying with BS EN 837 part 1 (1998). There should be an isolating valve within 2m of the autoclave. Steam pressure at the isolating valve should be controlled at 3.5 bar. It is recommended that culinary steam is supplied to autoclaves used for media (see also Section 4.2.2.4: steam).

Ventilation
The vicinity of the autoclave will require forced air in and extraction to the atmosphere. The extractor should be fitted with a fly screen (see Section 3.6: ventilation and temperature control). Because of the heat generated by an autoclave, the room in which the autoclave is sited should have 8 to 10 air changes per hour by the forced air in/extraction system. It is often necessary to install cooled air conditioning to extract heat from the autoclave room, particularly when the autoclave is sited in modern, well-insulated buildings.

Safety

It is a legal requirement for the autoclave to be checked annually under the Pressure Systems Regulations (2000). As a minimum the autoclave should have a quarterly in-house service carried out.

Autoclaves should be fitted with a thermal lock and mechanical lock to prevent the door being opened until the internal temperature has dropped to a safe level (maximum recommended temperature of 80°C). If there is a manual override facility (often key operated), this should only be used by authorised personnel in accordance with the manufacturer's instructions.

Suitable personal protective equipment, e.g. gloves, apron and face visor, must be available and in a suitable condition.

The waste disposal process must be validated to ensure sterility. Bags should be left open and containers left with loose lids during autoclaving to ensure effective steam penetration. Bagged waste should be kept in appropriate leak-proof containers whilst awaiting autoclaving.

The operating procedure should include daily safety checks as detailed by the manufacturer, e.g. door seal integrity, clear drainage.

References:
BS2646 Autoclaves for sterilisation in laboratories (5 parts)
BS3970 Autoclaves for sterilising and disinfecting medical products
BS EN 12347: 1998. Biotechnology. Performance criteria for steam sterilisers and autoclaves
HSE (2000) Safety of pressure systems. Pressure systems regulations 2000 approved code of practice
Safety at Autoclaves' HSE Guidance note PM73, HMSO 1990

5.4   Balances

These are portable pieces of equipment used to weigh media, chemicals and samples. They are also used for measuring volumes of diluent; in such cases they are usually referred to as gravimetric diluters.

Installation
Balances require a power supply and a vibration-free level bench away from sources of air disturbance.

Safety

Best practice demands that for the weighing of powders and potentially harmful chemicals, dust containment or extraction (which can be a recirculation system incorporating filters) is used to protect laboratory workers and minimise laboratory contamination. Use of personal dust masks will only protect the user and not those in the immediate vicinity.

5.5   Bunsen burners

Bunsen burners are used as part of aseptic technique and to sterilise instruments by dry heat or flaming in alcohol. A Bunsen flame is also used to heat fix organisms on microscope slides prior to staining.

Installation

Sufficient numbers of gas points should be provided at relevant locations where required to avoid excessive lengths of tubing over bench tops. Cooled air conditioning may be required in rooms where several Bunsen burners are in use.

Safety

Lit Bunsen burners must not be left unattended. When not in actual use, the air hole must be closed to produce a yellow flame which is more clearly visible. On some models a pilot flame feature can be used. The condition of the tubing should be inspected regularly and damaged tubing replaced.

If an LPG supply is used this must be located outside the building in a secure tamper proof enclosure.

The use of Bunsen burners in safety cabinets is not recommended since it can disturb the air flow and damage the filters. Use of sterile disposable or pre-sterilised implements may be more appropriate. If it is necessary to use the Bunsen burner in a safety cabinet, it must have a small flame so that air flow is not disturbed and the flame should be shrouded to protect the filters. Ideally it should be remotely, e.g. foot-operated.

5.6   Centrifuges

Centrifuges are used to separate suspended particles, in particular microorganisms, from liquids by centrifugal force.

Installation

Centrifuges may be bench or floor mounted and should preferably be sited away from balances and microscopes to minimise the effect of vibration. Centrifuge weight and size should be considered when determining siting. Centrifuges require a power supply.

Safety

Centrifuges must be operated and maintained in accordance with the manufacturer's instructions. Personnel using centrifuges must be trained in safe operation procedures, since incorrect use may result in a major accident. In order to prevent escape or leakage of biological materials, the vessel or rotor head should be sealed. Modern centrifuges have these safety features incorporated. Centrifuge tubes should be capped to improve safety. Consideration should be given to alternative designs of centrifuge tube, e.g. screw cap. Centrifuge tubes and buckets must be balanced before use. All centrifuges must be regularly serviced and maintained by suitably authorised service engineers.

Reference: BS EN 12457:1999+A1 2009 Centrifuges: Common safety requirements

5.7 Colony counters

This is an instrument used to assist in counting colonies on agar plates. Manual colony counters consist of an illuminated light source and magnifier with an electronic pressure pad or pen that registers the count. Computer imaging colony counters (comprised of computer algorithms and cameras to detect and record colonies) are available.

Installation

Most colony counters require a 13 amp electrical supply. There should be sufficient space for the colony counter, Petri dishes and worksheets on the bench.

Safety

Safe working practices must be applied when handling contaminated plates, and the colony counter should be disinfected after use according to the manufacturer's instructions. Prolonged use of colony counters may lead to operator fatigue. Therefore, sufficient breaks should be taken. Adjustable seating may be required. Consideration should be given to the safety implications when using colony counters which have a display screen (see Section 5.8 - Display Screen Equipment).

5.8 Computers and computer controlled equipment

Many laboratories use computer systems to manage the data in the form of a Laboratory Information Management System (LIMS) and some more sophisticated systems are linked to computers to analyse results/collect data.

Installation

In some laboratory environments splash-proof keyboards or covers may be required. If significant quantities of powders are used, remote siting of disk drives and printers is recommended. Care needs to be taken to ensure that the ergonomics are correct with respect to seating position in relation to keyboard and monitor. Good lighting is required and glare from windows should be avoided. Anti-glare screens can be used if necessary. Some equipment may require an uninterrupted power supply (UPS) unit and/or surge protection and equipment suppliers will advise if required.

Safety

It is necessary to perform a risk assessment on the workstation and its use. This should take into account the display screen equipment, the furniture, the working environment and the frequency and length of use by operators.

References:
Health and Safety (Display Screen Equipment) Regulations. SI 1992 no. 2792.
Health and Safety Executive HSE (1998). Seating at Work HS (G) 57, 3rd edition. Health and Safety Executive HSE (1998). Lighting at Work HS (G) 38, 2nd edition.
HSE (2003). Work with display screen equipment: Health and safety (display screen equipment) regulations 1992 as amended by the Health and safety (miscellaneous amendment) regulations 2002. Guidance on regulations.

5.9   Conductivity meter

This is used in the microbiology laboratory to assess the purity of the purified water by measuring the concentration of charged particles.

Installation
These are normally portable appliances, either battery operated or run off a 13-amp power supply.

Safety
There are no specific safety operations for this equipment.

5.10 Dust hoods

These are units used for the weighing out of powders such as dehydrated culture media and reagents. They are not to be used for hazardous chemicals and solvents, which must be handled in a fume cupboard. Fume cupboards have a higher safety specification, see section 5.12.

Installation
These are normally portable bench-top appliances with a 13 amp plug. The dust hood should be positioned away from excessive draughts.

Safety

The filters will need to be regularly replaced to ensure effective functioning. The manufacturer's instructions should be followed for filter replacement. It is also advisable to wear safety glasses and a disposable dust mask and disposable gloves when changing filters.

5.11 Freezers

These are pieces of equipment used for frozen storage of samples and cultures.

Installation

Hard wiring is preferred for larger freezers. However, smaller equipment may be portable and generally has a 13 amp plug. They should be located on the floor and preferably should be moveable for cleaning and maintenance. Location on bench tops is not recommended because this can lead to cleaning problems and some units can be extremely heavy and may collapse the bench. Stacking of several freezers may exceed floor loading specifications.

Heat is generated by these items of equipment. They should be sited in a large laboratory area to minimise heat build-up which could cause problems in temperature control or even total failure of the equipment. Appropriate moveable racking should be installed for 'walk in' freezer rooms.

Safety

Freezers must be properly spark guarded if used for storage of flammable solvents.

Walk-in freezer rooms require door handles that can be operated from inside the room. Panic alarms and external warning indicators of occupancy are also advantageous. Temperature distribution in walk-in rooms is significantly improved by fan circulation.

Personnel using walk in freezers may require thermal jackets. Insulated gloves must be worn when handling samples in -70°C freezers and for prolonged handling of samples in -20°C freezers. A safe working system (e.g. a 'buddy' system) should be adopted to monitor and control the length of time personnel spend in 'walk in' freezers.

5.12 Fume cupboards

Fume cupboards are designed to protect workers from harmful chemicals or dusts. They are used for some chemical work and for extraction of fumes from oil baths.

Installation

Fume cupboards are normally permanently installed (although portable units are available) with all services (gas, electricity, drainage, water, vacuum) supplied. They should be sited away from draughts. Permanent fume cupboards should be installed by a competent authorised engineer. The extract pipe needs to discharge well above the roof of the building, and away from opening windows and food operations. Allowance needs to be made for an air inlet to the laboratory if a fume cupboard is installed.

Safety

All fume cupboards must be regularly maintained and serviced according to the manufacturer's instructions to ensure continued safe operation. Ductless fume cupboards that work by re-circulating air through filters will need regular replacement of filters. This replacement should be carried out in a safe manner. The use of Bunsen burners in fume cupboards is not recommended since it can disturb the air flow and damage the filters. If it is necessary to use the Bunsen burner in fume cupboards, it must have a small flame so that air flow is not disturbed.

Reference: BS EN 14175 Fume cupboards parts 1-6.

5.13 Gas cylinders

Gas cylinders may be used where an alternative gaseous environment is used for incubation of cultures or modified atmosphere packaging. LPG is used as an alternative for natural gas where a supply is not available.

Installation

Gas cylinders should be located in a cool place, preferably in a purpose-built, well ventilated outside structure and secured so that they cannot be knocked over. It is better to pipe gas supplies permanently to the laboratory rather than use cylinders in the laboratory itself (see Section 4.2.3.2: cylinder gases). Cylinders must not be connected directly to any apparatus but require a system of pressure-reducing valves and flame trap devices (for inflammable gases). Note that flammable gas cylinders have left hand threads.

Safety

Personnel should be trained in the safe handling of gas cylinders. Cylinders should be moved using special trolleys and should always be transported and secured in an upright position.

Gas cylinders are very heavy and should not be carried up stairs. Where a lift is available it should be used. Ideally they should not be moved over long distances.

If a gas cylinder falls over, the safety valve may be broken, and could result in the cylinder acting as a trajectory, causing serious damage and injury. Uncontrolled leakage of gases (e.g. N_2, CO_2) into small, poorly ventilated spaces may lead to asphyxiation.

References:
BOC handbook 'Safety in the use of compressed gas cylinders'. Approved code of practice
'Safety of transportable gas containers' HMSO, ISBN 0 11 88555158.
The highly flammable liquids and liquefied petroleum gases regulations 1972.
Pressure systems and transportable gas containers regulations, SI 1989 no. 2169,
(See also Section 4.2.3.2: cylinder gases)

5.14 Glassware washing machines

These are machines designed for washing laboratory glassware. They can be programmed for different wash programs to include a purified water rinse. A range of glassware racks can be purchased for glassware of different dimensions.

Installation
These produce moist air and should be sited where there is good ventilation. Hot and cold water (check pressure required), drainage and a power supply (3-phase or single phase) are required. Washing machines are best sited against an outside wall since many machines are fitted with an air vent. Sufficient space is required to open the door and load trays of glassware. Some machines require a softened or deionised water supply.

Safety
There are no specific safety operations for this equipment. However, some of the detergents and other chemicals needed may have safety requirements for use.

5.15 Heating blocks

These are portable appliances used for heat treatments of samples and reagents in tubes of different dimensions. A range of blocks are available to hold tubes of different volume and dimension. They can be used as an alternative for water baths and generally have a smaller footprint.

Installation
An electrical supply is required.

Safety
Heating blocks should be located on heat resistant surfaces, and the usual precautions should be taken for handling hot equipment and liquids.

5.16 Hotplates

These are portable pieces of equipment used for heating media and solutions. They are thermostatically controlled and some incorporate a means of stirring the liquids.

Installation
An electrical supply is required. Some applications may require use of a fume cupboard (see Section 5.9: Fume cupboards). In any case, sufficient space should be allowed for easy access to the hotplate to avoid accidents.

Safety
Hotplates should be located on heat resistant surfaces, and the usual precautions should be taken for handling hot equipment and liquids.

5.17 Incubators

These are pieces of equipment used for storage and incubation of samples and cultures.

Installation
Hard wiring is preferred for larger items of equipment (i.e. 'walk-in' facilities). However, smaller equipment may be portable and generally has a 13 amp plug. They should be located on the floor or on a stand and preferably should be moveable for cleaning and maintenance. Location on bench tops is not recommended because this can lead to cleaning problems and some units, e.g. water jacketed incubators, can be extremely heavy and may collapse the bench. Stacking of several heavy incubators may exceed floor-loading specifications. Appropriate moveable racking should be installed for 'walk in' incubator rooms.

Heat is generated by these items of equipment. They should be sited in a large laboratory area or in a well ventilated 'incubation' room to minimise heat build-up that could cause problems in temperature control or even total failure of the equipment. Temperature distribution in walk-in rooms is significantly improved by fan circulation. Incubator rooms should have a fail-safe cut out thermostat to prevent extremes of temperature.

Safety
Walk-in incubation rooms require door handles that can be operated from inside. Panic alarms and external warning indicators of occupancy are also advantageous. There are no specific safety operations for this equipment.

5.18 Laminar flow cabinets

Horizontal and vertical laminar flow cabinets are available for aseptic work. Note that these are not safety cabinets and must not be used for manipulation of cultures of microorganisms.

Installation
Laminar flow cabinets generally re-circulate the air and therefore do not require external ducting. A power source is required (usually single phase 13 amp plug). Laminar flow cabinets are easily affected by draughts so should be sited away from draughts and areas of high activity.

Safety
Laminar flow cabinets must be regularly maintained and serviced according to the manufacturer's instructions to ensure continued safe operation. The use of Bunsen burners in laminar air flow cabinets is not recommended since it can disturb the air flow and damage the filters. Use of sterile disposable or pre-sterilised implements may be more appropriate. If it is necessary to use the Bunsen burner in a laminar air flow cabinet, it must have a small flame so that air flow is not disturbed and the flame should be shrouded to protect the filters. Ideally it should be remotely, e.g. foot-operated.

5.19 Media dispenser

A media dispenser is used to dispense pre-defined volumes of liquids that may be later autoclaved.

Installation
Some media dispensers are linked to a media preparator, in which case the two pieces of equipment must be compatible and sufficient space made available for their co-location.

Safety
Normal considerations associated with handling liquids in association with electrical equipment apply.

5.20 Media preparator

Media preparators are used to sterilise large batches of media (greater than 1L) and consist of a heating vessel, water jacket and continuous stirring device. They are often connected to a plate pouring machine.

Installation
Media preparators require power, water supply, drainage and a steam exhaust pipe. They are normally permanently sited. Power is usually via a 13 amp plug but direct connection via a switched hard wire connection is preferable. The steam exhaust needs to be piped to a drain, preferably outside or to a ventilated area.

Safety
Media preparators are subject to the Pressure systems and transportable gas containers regulations, SI 1989 (No 2169) and require annual checks for insurance purposes. See Guideline 9 Section 4.13.

References:
Pressure systems and transportable gas containers regulations, SI 1989 no. 2169.
'Safety at Autoclaves' HSE Guidance note PM73, HMSO 1990.

5.21 Microscopes (optical microscopes)

These are used to examine microorganisms and samples under higher levels of magnification to enable viewing of structures not visible to the naked eye.

Installation
Microscopes should be installed in a dry, clean, dust-free environment away from sources of vibration, e.g. centrifuges and stomachers. A single-phase power supply is required. The operator should be provided with an adjustable seat, especially if use of the microscope is prolonged. Direct sunlight can adversely affect the viewing of specimens, and a darkened room may be required for specific applications such as fluorescence microscopy.

Safety
There are no specific safety operations for this equipment. However, consideration must be given to the safe disposal of contaminated and broken slides and cover slips. Refer to Section 6.7, Waste Disposal for further details.

5.22 Microwave ovens

Specialised microwave ovens have been developed for sterilisation and melting of culture media and moisture tests. Domestic microwave ovens are not recommended for use in the laboratory for media preparation since they have insufficient safety features and can cause serious accidents with boiling of media.

Installation
Microwave ovens require only a 13 amp power supply.

Safety
Specialist advice should be obtained because of specific safety requirements involved. The usual precautions should be taken for handling hot equipment and liquids.

5.23 Ovens

These are used for drying of glassware and dry sterilisation of equipment.

Installation
Hot air ovens can either be hard wired or fitted with a 13 amp plug. All ovens should be positioned in a convenient position for access, i.e. free from laboratory traffic. The temperature output of the equipment needs to be considered in view of its proximity to other equipment (e.g. refrigerators).

Safety
If the ovens are left unsupervised, some form of over-temperature protection should be installed, e.g. additional adjustable or non-adjustable thermostat or thermal fuse. The usual precautions should be taken for handling hot equipment and liquids.

Reference: BS 2648 (1955 Confirmed 2006). Performance requirements for electrically heated laboratory drying ovens.

5.24 pH meters

pH meters are used to measure the pH of prepared media and samples.

Installation
These may be battery operated hand held devices or bench top models fitted with a 13 amp plug.

Safety

There are no specific safety operations for this equipment.

5.25 Plate pourers

Plate pourers are used to dispense set volumes of pre-sterilised media in petri dishes. They may be stand alone or connected to an agar preparator.

Installation

A 13 amp supply and a level bench are usually required for plate pourers. Plate pourers can take up a large area of bench space. Some units are connected to a refrigeration unit, which is better mounted beneath the bench. To avoid contamination problems the pourer should be located in a clean, dust free environment.

Safety

There are no specific safety operations for this equipment. Since media should be dispensed at temperatures less than 50°C, there should be no need for specific precautions for the handling of hot liquids.

5.26 Refrigerators

These are used for storage and incubation of samples and cultures

Installation

Hard wiring is preferred for larger items of equipment (i.e. 'walk-in' facilities). However, smaller equipment may be portable and generally has a 13 amp plug. They can be positioned on the floor or on a stand and preferably should be moveable for cleaning and maintenance. Some models are heavy and consideration of this must be made if locating the unit on a bench. Stacking of several heavy refrigerators may exceed floor-loading specifications.

Heat is generated by these items of equipment. They should be located in a sufficiently well ventilated area to minimise heat build-up, which could cause problems in temperature control or even total failure of the equipment. Temperature distribution in walk-in rooms is significantly improved by fan circulation. Refrigerator rooms should have a fail-safe cut out thermostat to prevent extremes of temperature. Appropriate moveable racking should be installed for 'walk in' refrigerator rooms.

Safety

Refrigerators must be properly spark guarded if used for storage of inflammable solvents.

Walk-in refrigerator rooms require door handles that can be operated from inside the room. Panic alarms and external warning indicators of occupancy are also advantageous. Note that dry ice should not be stored in a walk-in chiller because of the risk of build up of CO_2 and asphyxiation of personnel.

5.27 Safety cabinets

Safety cabinets provide operator and laboratory environment protection for manipulation of microorganisms.

There are 3 main types:

Class 1: Open fronted exhaust cabinets, which protect the worker but not the work within the cabinet.

Class 2: Open fronted vertical flow cabinets with inflow to protect the worker and work within the cabinet.

Class 3: Totally enclosed with glove ports. Used for category 3 organisms or above, unlikely to be required in a food microbiology laboratory.

Installation
All safety cabinets should be installed and commissioned by a competent authorised engineer. Cabinets are usually quite large and require sufficient width, depth and height for installation. Consideration should be given to laboratory traffic, doors and windows that will affect air movement in the vicinity of the cabinet and its level of safe performance. If located on a bench it should be strong enough to support the weight of the cabinet.

Class 1 and 2 cabinets are normally ducted to the outside atmosphere. Therefore, the location of existing ventilation ducts and passage of people should be taken into account. A single phase 13 amp supply is required. Similar considerations for installation apply to Class 3 as for Class 1 and 2 cabinets.

Safety
All safety cabinets must be regularly maintained and serviced according to the manufacturer's instructions to ensure continued safe operation. If the cabinet is relocated or air flows around the cabinet change, then the cabinet must be decommissioned. In-use testing under representative laboratory conditions should be carried out. More information is available from the references below. All users must be properly trained on the safe operation and use of the cabinet.

All operators should be aware of the routine requirements and emergency procedure in the event of a spillage. There are special procedures required for emergency decontamination, which may include fumigation, and information is available from the references below. The manufacturers may also recommend specific procedures and advice.

The use of a Bunsen burner in safety cabinets is not recommended since it can disturb the air flow and damage the filters. Use of sterile disposable or pre-sterilised implements is more appropriate. If it is necessary to use the Bunsen burner in a safety cabinet, it should be located at the back and the flame should be shrouded to protect the filters. The burner must used with the flame at its lowest workable level so that air flow is disturbed as little as possible.

References:
Advisory Committee on Dangerous Pathogens (2001). The management, design and operation of microbiological containment laboratories. Health and Safety Executive.
BS EN 12469: 2000 Biotechnology. Performance criteria for microbiology safety cabinets
BS 5726 (2005). Microbiological Safety Cabinets. Information to be supplied by the purchaser to the vendor and to the installer and siting and use of cabinets. Recommendations and guidance.

5.28 Steamers

Koch or Arnold steamers are electric, gas or steam coil heated boxes containing water used for re-melting media or steaming media during preparation.

Installation
Steam produced should be extracted to atmosphere. For safety reasons, steamers should be located away from 'gangways' in the laboratory and power sockets should be positioned away from the moist environment.

Safety
During operation the water level must be sufficient to ensure that the heating elements are kept covered. The usual precautions should be taken for handling hot equipment and liquids.

5.28 Stomachers

Stomachers are used in preparation of non-liquid samples. They mechanically blend samples in a sterile plastic bag to release the microorganisms from the sample into the diluent.

Installation

A 13 amp power supply is required. This equipment may cause vibration and should not be on the same bench as balances or microscopes. Allowance should be made for sufficient space for baskets of samples next to the stomacher.

Safety

There are no specific safety operations for this equipment.

5.30 Thermal cyclers (also known as PCR blocks)

Thermal cyclers are used for polymerase chain reaction (PCR) analysis.

Installation

PCR blocks have specific quality requirements. It is recommended that advice is sought from the supplier and/or an experienced laboratory before introduction of PCR-based methods. Consideration should be given in the location of these instruments to reduce the possibility of cross contamination of food samples with previously amplified DNA. They are generally fitted with a 13 amp power plug.

Safety

There are no specific safety operations for basic thermal cyclers, although care should be taken when removing reaction plates/tubes if the instrument surfaces are hot. For real time instruments there may be further precautions that need to be taken, and the manufacturer's instructions should be consulted to determine other possible hazards relating to the specific equipment. These may include ensuring that the block is at room temperature before cleaning the wells and allowing the halogen lamp to cool prior to replacing the bulb.

5.31 UV lamps

UV lamps may be used in chromatography, microscopy or observation of microbial colonies (e.g. MUG media for *E. coli* identification).

Installation

A 13 amp power supply may be required.

Safety

Direct and reflected UV light can be damaging to eyes and skin. Some UV lamps will have in-built safety features to protect the user. However, if this is not the case, users must wear suitable protective gloves and eye/face guards for UV protection.

5.32 Vacuum pumps

Portable vacuum pumps may be required for filtration apparatus or culture freeze drying.

Installation
A 13 amp power supply is required. This equipment may cause bench vibration and should not be on the same bench as balances or microscopes.

Safety
Oil mist filters should be fitted to minimise environmental contamination. The pumps should be maintained to ensure safe use. If excessively noisy, ear protection should be used.

5.33 Water/oil baths

Water baths are used for incubation of bottled test samples and tempering agar. Boiling water baths can be used for steaming and sterilising temperature sensitive media. Oil baths are used when higher temperatures are required.

Installation
Water/oil baths require a 13 amp socket. Oil baths are normally sited in a fume cupboard.

Safety
Manufacturers' recommendations for use of the correct oil in relation to temperatures required must be followed to avoid the production of noxious fumes. The usual precautions should be taken for handling hot equipment and liquids.

5.34 Water purification equipment

Water can be purified using stills, deoinisers or reverse osmosis units. The water is used for media and reagent preparation.

Installation
All water purification systems require a potable water supply. The manufacturer's instructions should be followed for installation and maintenance for these systems. This may include checking that the water supply has an adequate and consistent pressure. If the laboratory is located in a hard water area the equipment will require more frequent maintenance to ensure effective operation. Most water purification systems require a power supply.

Stills should be hard wired because power consumption can be high. Adequate drainage is required. Stills should be securely fixed to the wall to allow gravity feed to a water storage container. Deionisers and reverse osmosis units vary in size and can be used to produce water on demand or have a large water reservoir for storage of pure water. They require an electrical supply and a significantly strong support for the water reservoir.

Safety

Stills normally have an automatic thermal cut out for water supply failure and a built-in thermostat for temperature control. There are no specific safety requirements for deionisers or reverse osmosis units.

6. DOCUMENTATION

Having designed and constructed the laboratory, the manager should ensure that all necessary documentation systems are in place and maintained. These must support and assist the consistent operation of correct safe working practices by all staff, provide evidence of compliance and assist investigations in the event of failures.

Much of the information within the laboratory documentation (e.g. in standard operating procedures SOPs) will be method and quality related. Safety procedures specific to an operation should be stressed in the SOP.

Specific detailed documentation must cover the following, all of which have a relation to safety:

- Safe microbiology laboratory practices

- Microbiology containment to include access for non-microbiology laboratory personnel

- Safety aspects relating to laboratory equipment including use, commissioning, servicing and maintenance requirements

- Training of personnel

- Laboratory housekeeping and hygiene including laboratory environmental monitoring

- Laboratory disinfection procedures

- Waste handling and disposal

- Handling of cultures

- Laundering of used laboratory coats

- COSHH

- Risk assessments

- Transport of microbiological cultures (HSE 1986)

- Emergency procedures

6.1   Safe microbiology laboratory practices

These are a set of simple rules to follow when working in the laboratory to help ensure that microorganisms are handled appropriately. The basic rules should be clearly documented and should ideally be posted close to the laboratory entrance as a reminder to laboratory staff and visitors.

- A properly fastened laboratory coat of an appropriate design must be worn at all times in the laboratory and removed when leaving the laboratory

- When leaving the laboratory hands must be washed after removing the laboratory coat

- Hands must be washed immediately after handling contaminated materials, dealing with spillages or if hand contamination is suspected

- There must be no eating, drinking, chewing, smoking or application of cosmetics in the laboratory

- Food and drinks intended for consumption must not be stored in the laboratory and any food or drink from the laboratory must be disposed of as food waste

- Mouth pipetting must be forbidden. Self adhesive labels and other stationery must be used to eliminate the need for licking of envelopes etc.

- Doors to the laboratory should be kept closed

- Contaminated materials should be stored in a safe manner prior to decontamination before disposal, i.e. in a leak proof container

- Cultures should be appropriately handled and lidded to prevent inadvertent spillage

- Benches should be cleaned and disinfected after each use.

- All minor cuts and lesions must be covered with a water proof plaster; if on the hand, gloves must be worn. Consideration needs to be given to temporary exclusion from laboratory work or transferring to alternative work for more serious wounds until they are sufficiently healed.

6.2   Microbiology containment to include access for non-microbiology laboratory personnel

This will form part of the COSHH assessment for the laboratory and must contain details of procedures in place to minimise the potential risk of contamination to staff and visitors in the laboratory, the laboratory environment and the external environment (refer to Section 2.1.4 for further details on containment). The documentation should include evidence that sufficient training has been given to the laboratory staff at an appropriate level according to their job role.

Various signs and notices should be displayed at the laboratory entrance. These would include:

- Biohazard signs
- Restricted access notices
- Notices requiring protective clothing to be worn
- Any additional specific temporary (or permanent) warning notices, e.g. wet floors

In addition to the laboratory staff, non-microbiology laboratory personnel require access to the laboratory from time to time and on occasion this may be without supervision. Such personnel may include:

- Cleaning staff
- Contract maintenance/repair personnel
- Service engineers
- Builders
- Computer services personnel
- Security staff

It is important to ensure that non-microbiology personnel comply with basic hygiene and safety requirements, e.g. wear protective clothing and wash hands when leaving the laboratory. It is also essential that they have sufficient instruction or supervision to maintain the integrity of the laboratory environment, equipment and work in progress. Documentation covering the key points for such instruction should be available.

6.3 Safety aspects relating to laboratory equipment including use, commissioning, servicing and maintenance requirements

All equipment should be commissioned, serviced and maintained according to the manufacturers' instructions. There are specific pieces of equipment which have legal or essential safety requirements (see Section 5). Equipment of note is:

- Autoclaves
- Centrifuges
- Display screen equipment (DSE)
- Fume cupboards
- Gas cylinders
- Laminar air flow cabinets
- Safety cabinets

All safety related aspects of equipment use should be included in the documentation, either in a stand alone safety document or as part of a standard operating procedure (SOP). Records of the maintenance and servicing must be kept and readily retrievable. Training records for staff authorised to use equipment must be kept and updated as and when necessary (refer to section 6.4 below on training).

6.4   Training of personnel

Well planned and executed programmes for staff training are essential to ensure:

- The safe operation of the laboratory
- Safe and competent practice of microbiological methods and procedures

Training schedules should encompass every operation of the laboratory and the appropriate documented procedures used as the basis for such training. Records should be kept indicating that training has been given to named individuals in appropriate areas, date the training was completed, the name of the trainer, and the signature of trainer and trainee. Part of the criteria for measuring the success of the specific training item should be an understanding of safety requirements.

Training should encompass:

- Safe microbiology laboratory practices
- Knowledge of safety documentation relevant to the tasks carried out
- Use of equipment
- Accident procedures
- Handling of waste
- Laboratory disinfection procedures
- Housekeeping
- Sample handling and records

Appropriate emphasis should be placed on safety in all laboratory documentation. An additional section on retraining should be included. Retraining/refresher training would be required for a major change in equipment/ methods, return to work after a prolonged absence, and infrequently carried out procedures.

Reference: Anon. Biological agents: managing risks in laboratories and health care premises. HSE. www.hse.gov.uk/biosafety/biologagents.pdf

6.5   Laboratory housekeeping and hygiene including laboratory environmental monitoring

Laboratories must be kept clean and tidy at all times. Accumulations of dust, debris and waste materials can give rise to a safety and/or cross contamination hazard. Housekeeping schedules and procedures should be drawn up to include all laboratory areas and equipment. Schedules should take account of:

- Frequency of task

- Responsibility for the task

- Detailed description of what is required

- Cleaning aids to be used

- Method of waste disposal

The efficacy of the housekeeping and microbiological containment can be monitored by the use of swabs, and air (settle) plates. This should be included in the housekeeping procedure. Documents to record the results, action limits and corrective actions must be kept.

In addition, procedures for general personal hygiene should be documented. These could include hand washing requirements, appropriate dress and footwear and the tying back of long hair. Other local rules such as the wearing of jewellery could also be documented here.

6.6   Laboratory disinfection procedures

Laboratory benches must be kept clean at all times. Routine disinfection procedures require documentation. This should include:

- Disinfection of benches before and after use,

- Disinfection of trays/containers used for incubation and/or storage of plates

- Steeping of pipettes and other equipment

- Spillage procedures

- Decontamination of used contaminated glass, e.g. microscope slides

The procedures need to include type and strength of disinfectant and contact time required for effective decontamination, as well as the frequency the disinfectant needs to be changed. Some disinfectants may be toxic, irritant or corrosive and appropriate protective measures must be taken (such as protective equipment, e.g. gloves and safety glasses) when handling the disinfectant, especially at high concentrations. Consideration should also be given to whether the disinfectant is incompatible with the items/solutions to be decontaminated. When decontaminating objects by immersion, they must be sufficiently covered with the disinfectant.

There are different types of disinfectant available but hypochlorite solutions are commonly used. 1,000 ppm is suitable for routine disinfection, 2,500 ppm for disinfectant jars and 10,000 ppm for culture spillage. The manufacturer's instructions should be followed for other types of disinfectant.

There will be additional requirements for disinfection and/or fumigation of safety cabinets. The procedure must be documented.

6.7   Waste handling and disposal

Methods of disposal of contaminated waste vary between facilities. However, there is a legal requirement to ensure that it is disposed of in such a manner in order to render it harmless. Further information on the legislation is detailed in Section 2. Procedures for decontamination of contaminated waste must be validated and documented. These records (e.g. autoclave validation and ongoing processing records) must be kept.

There should be procedures available for the disposal of the following:

- Contaminated solid cultures, e.g. petri dishes and slopes
- Contaminated liquid cultures, e.g. broths
- Food samples
- Sharps, e.g. broken glass and hypodermic needles
- Contaminated plastics, e.g. loops and pipettes
- Contaminated glass slides
- Solvents and other noxious chemicals
- Diagnostic test kits

6.8   Handling of cultures

Positive control cultures used in the laboratory will be supplied in a variety of formats including freeze dried in ampoules (from culture collections), on paper discs, in a gel format, and in lenticules. The supplier should provide instructions on the safe culturing and initial growth of the organisms. These instructions should be followed. Safety requirements for the use and disposal of control cultures should be documented.

6.9   Laundering of used laboratory coats

There should be a documented procedure for the decontamination and washing of laboratory coats. For containment level 2 it is not necessary to routinely disinfect or autoclave laboratory coats prior to laundering. However, the coats should be segregated from other laundry and dispatched to the laundry in a manner which prevents the need for the laundry to sort the coats before washing. A hot washing cycle is required for laboratory coats.

If major spillages occur causing the coat to become grossly contaminated, it should be autoclaved before laundering.

6.10 Risk assessments

In microbiology laboratories, risk assessment documentation needs to cover all aspects of the work carried out, including handling of biological agents and chemicals used as well as other hazards such as the use of steam or a UV light source. There are 5 key steps to follow when carrying out risk assessments:

Step 1   Identify the hazards involved

Step 2   Decide who might be harmed and how

Step 3   Evaluate the risks and decide the precautions

Step 4   Record the precautions needed and how they will be implemented at a practical level

Step 5   Review the assessment and update as and when necessary

The definition of a risk assessment is "an indication of the hazards present in an undertaking and an estimation of the extent of the risks involved, taking into account whatever precautions are already taken". A hazard is defined as something that has the potential to cause harm (or loss); examples are chemicals and electricity. A risk is the likelihood that somebody could be harmed by this hazard, together with an indication of how serious this harm could be.

Risk assessments have to be reviewed regularly and when there is reason to suspect that the risk assessment is no longer valid, or if there has been a significant change in the work to which the risk assessment relates, or if the results of any monitoring that has been carried out indicate it to be necessary.

When carrying out these risk assessments, the following aspects need to be considered:

- The hazardous properties of the substance

- Information on health effects provided by the supplier, including information contained in any relevant safety data sheet

- The level, type and duration of exposure

- The circumstances of the work including the amount of the substance involved

- Activities, such as maintenance, where there is the potential for a high level of exposure

- Any relevant occupational exposure standard, maximum exposure limit or similar occupational exposure limit

- The effect of preventive and control measures

- The results of relevant health surveillance

- The results of monitoring of exposure

- In circumstances where the work will involve exposure to more than one substance hazardous to health, the risk presented by exposure to such substances in combination

- The approved classification of any biological agent

- Such additional information as the employer may need in order to complete the risk assessment.

Refer to section 6.10 above for more details on COSHH risk assessments.

Biological agents

If the experimental work involves handling biological agents, then the risk assessments must take the following points into consideration:

- The hazard group of the biological agent

- The form in which the agent may be present - e.g. which infectious stage or spores

- How and where the agents are present

- How any potential disease (associated with the agent) may be caused and how it can be transmitted

- The likelihood of exposure of the laboratory staff (to the agent in question) and the consequent disease

These points will determine the protective measures required to ensure that the organism is contained in a safe manner. Many of the protocols used in a microbiology laboratory will involve a combination of biological agents and chemicals. This should be taken into account when deciding the appropriate safety precautions needed.

Further considerations

In addition to the general risk assessments specific risk assessments have to be done in respect of young persons and new or expectant mothers.

Young people

Young people may be present in a laboratory as workers, students, or trainees or on work experience. A young person is defined as anyone under 18 years old. A child is anyone who has not reached the official age at which they may leave school, just before or just after their 16th birthday.

Under the health and safety law, you must assess the risk to young people **before** they start work or work experience and inform them what those risks are. In addition, the parents/guardians of children still of compulsory school age must also be informed of the key findings of the risk assessment and the control measures introduced before the child starts work.

Young people can be at greater risk from hazardous work activities due to lack of psychological or physical maturity, or lack of experience, training and awareness, and may not pay enough attention to safety.

When assessing the risk the following points must be taken into account:

- How the workplace is fitted and laid out (and the particular site where they work)
- What type of work equipment will be used and how will it be handled
- How the work and processes involved are organised
- The need to assess and provide heath and safety training
- The degree of supervision available for the duration of the employment or work experience
- The nature of any physical, biological and chemical agents they will be exposed to, for how long and to what extent
- The risk of certain hazards

The extent of the risks identified will help decide whether it is necessary to restrict certain aspects of the job. The overall rule is that young people under 18 must not be allowed to do work which:

- Cannot be adapted to meet any physical or mental limitations they may have

- Exposes them to substances that are toxic or cause cancer

- Exposes them to radiation

- Involves a risk of accidents which they are unlikely to recognise because of their lack of experience, training or sufficient attention to safety

- Involves extreme heat, noise or vibration

The restrictions do not apply to young people over the minimum school leaving age where the work they are doing is necessary for training, the work is properly supervised by a competent person and the risks are reduced to the lowest level, so far as reasonably practicable.

Risk assessments need to be reviewed if the nature of the work changes or if it is no longer valid. It is not necessary to review the risk assessments each time a young person is hired, provided it takes into account the characteristics of young people.

References:
The right start INDG364
Young people at work; a guide for employers HSG165

New or expectant mothers

Under the health and safety law, you must assess the risk to female employees who are, or in the future could be, a new or expectant mother.

These are:

- Women of childbearing age who are pregnant

- Women of childbearing age who in future could be pregnant

- Women who have given birth within the previous six months

- Women who are breastfeeding

When assessing the risks for new and expectant mothers the possible hazards in processes, working conditions, and physical, biological and chemical agents must be taken into account, for example:

- shocks, vibration or movement

- manual handling of loads where there is a risk of injury

- ionising radiation

- extremes of cold and heat

- movement and postures

- substances labelled

    - R40   possible risk of irreversible effects
    - R45   may cause cancer
    - R46   may cause heritable genetic damage
    - R61   may cause harm to the unborn child
    - R63   possible risk of harm to the unborn child
    - R64   may cause harm to breastfed babies

- any biological agent of hazard group 2, 3 and 4; and

- mercury and mercury derivatives

If the risk assessments indicate that there is a significant risk to the health and safety of a new or expectant mother, actions must be taken to remove the hazard or prevent exposure to the risk. If this is not possible and there is a significant risk which goes beyond the level of risk to be expected outside the workplace, then consideration must be given to adjust the working conditions and/or hours. If that is not possible, or it would not avoid the risk, suitable alternative work must be offered; or the employee may be suspended from work on paid leave to protect her and her child's safety.

Risk assessments need to be reviewed if the nature of the work changes or if it is no longer valid. Although any hazards are likely to remain constant, the possibility of damage to the foetus as a result of a hazard will vary at different stages of pregnancy. There are different risks to consider for workers who are breastfeeding.

The Workplace Regulations (Health, Safety and Welfare) 1992 require suitable rest facilities to be provided for workers who are pregnant or breastfeeding.

References:
A guide for new and expectant mothers who work. IND373
New and expectant mother at work, a guide for employers HS (G) 122
Advisory committee on dangerous pathogens: Infection risks to new and expectant mothers in the workplace, a guide for employers

Further information on risk assessment can be found in the following references:

Five steps to risk assessment. Leaflet INDG163 (rev1), HSE Books 1998 (single copy free or priced packs of 10 ISBN 0 7176 1565 0) or available online at: www.hse.gov.uk/pubns/INDG163.pdf

A guide to risk assessment requirements: Common provisions in health and safety law. Leaflet INDG218, HSE Books 1996 (single copy free or priced packs of 5 ISBN 0 7176 1211 2) or available online at: www.hse.gov.uk/pubns/INDG218.pdf

6.11 COSHH

Using chemicals or other hazardous substances at work can put people's health at risk, so the law requires employers to control exposure to substances hazardous to health. They have to protect both employees and others who may be exposed by complying with the Control of Substances Hazardous to Health Regulations 2002. In microbiology laboratories there are two aspects that need to be considered:

- Control of the biological agents (microorganisms)

  Refer to Section 2 for details on biological agents.

- Control of chemical reagents used (culture media and test reagents)

  Hazardous substances that need to be considered include:
  - Substances used directly in work activities
  - Substances generated during work activities
  - Naturally occurring substances
  - Biological agents such bacteria and other micro-organisms

The following 5 step procedure can be used to determine the controls required when working with hazardous materials:

Step 1: Assess the risk

Step 1(a): Identify the hazardous substances used in a procedure

In the first step the substances and the associated risks are identified. The COSHH risk assessments are based on probable risks and not on potential risks, i.e. don't assume worst-case scenarios. The hazardous substances should include chemicals, reagents, media, gases and biological agents. For chemicals, reagents, media and gases check that the Material Safety Data Sheet (MSDS) is available. Section 9 on the MSDS shows the boiling point or the vapour pressure with the temperature (°C) at which this was measured (see exposure potential). Section 15 lists the correct risk phrases, whereas sections 2 and 3 of the MSDS refer to components of a mixture and should not be used.

You must also consider who is at risk and which groups of people, apart from trained analysts, are likely to come into contact with the substances, e.g. cleaners and contractors. Also consider if people are likely to respond differently to the substance, e.g. pregnant women and immuno-compromised people. If this is likely, make a comment or if necessary carry out a separate risk assessment.

Step 1(b): Determine the exposure potential

This is based on three elements: the quantity in use, the state of the substance and the operation.

	Score ->	0	1	2
Factors in exposure potential	A Quantity	Less than 1 g or ml	Between 1-500 g or ml	More than 500 g or ml
	B Physical form	Boiling point higher than 180°C	Boiling point between 80°C and >180°C	Boiling point below 180°C
		Pellets	Crystals or granules	Powders
		Dilute solutions		Concentrated solutions
		No skin absorption likely	Low skin absorption likely	Skin adsorption possible
	C Operation	Closed system	Partially open system	Open vessel
		Used at room temperature		Used at elevated temperatures
		Low risk of hazard occurring	Medium risk of hazard occurring	High risk of hazard occurring

Calculate the exposure potential (EP) by adding the three factors (EP= A+B+C).

> If EP ≤ 3, then EP is LOW
> If EP = 4, then the EP is MEDIUM
> If EP ≥ 5, then the EP is HIGH

However, where a Material Safety Data Sheet may suggest that prolonged or repeated exposure may have an adverse effect on health then a higher EP category may be assigned.

Step 1(c): Determine the "hazard group" (i.e. the potential to cause harm)

This is based on the risk phrases that are documented on the Material Safety Data Sheets (and also on the labels of chemical containers) that are available for all commercial chemical substances. There are four different risk ratings (see following table).

Hazard group		Risk phrases*
V	Very high	R26, R27, R28, R32, R33 R35, R39, R42, R45, R48, R49
H	High	R23, R24, R25, R29, R31, R34, R40, R41, R43, R46, R60, R61, R64, R68
M	Medium	R20, R21, R22, R36, R37, R38, R43, R62, R63, R65, R66, R67
L	Low	Substances with no associated risk phrases and which, after inspection of structure or of other data, cannot be classified as V, H, or M by analogy.

*Risk phrases R1 to R19, R30 and R44 refer to physical and chemical properties that must be considered in "Additional Information",
*Risk phrases R50 to R59 refer to the environmental impact of the chemicals which must be considered when identifying appropriate disposal routes.

For certain chemicals it will be necessary to check the workplace exposure limits (EH40/2005).

Step 1(d): Determine the overall risk assessment

In the last step determine the overall risk assessment taking into consideration exposure potential and risk rating using the matrix in table 3. It is important to remember that substances may have other hazardous properties, for example flammable, oxidising or explosive, which must also be controlled. Therefore the COSHH assessment should not be thought of in isolation from other hazards present as these may influence the control measures required.

Indicate also whether the need for health surveillance has been identified.

	Exposure potential		
Toxic rating	Low	Medium	High
V	2	3	3
H	2	2	3
M	1	2	2
L	1	1	2

Step 2: Prevent or adequately control exposure.

The COSHH regulations require that employers prevent exposure to substances hazardous to health, if it is reasonably practicable to do so. For substances with overall risk assessment of 2 or 3, consider the following hierarchy of control:

E -> Eliminate
- Is it possible to change the process or activity so that the substance is not needed or generated?

R -> Reduce or replace
- Is it possible to replace the substance with a safer alternative?
- Is it possible to obtain the substance in a safer form, e.g. pellets instead of fine powder?

I -> Isolate
- Work in local exhaust ventilation units (local exhaust ventilations (LEV) - fume cupboards)

C -> Controls
- Information
- Instruction (SOP and safe systems at work)
- Training

P -> Personal Protective Equipment
- Gloves
- Face masks

Further help can be obtained on the COSHH website (*www.coshh-essentials.org.uk*).

Step 3: Decide what precautions are needed

If prevention is not reasonably practicable, exposure must be adequately controlled. This is done considering control measures that are appropriate to the activity and that are consistent with the risk assessment.

Examples are:

- The use of appropriate work process systems and engineering controls
- Provision of suitable work equipment and materials

- Processes which minimise the amount of material used or produced
- Controlling of exposure at source, such as:
  - Local exhaust ventilation
  - Reducing the number of employees exposed to a minimum
  - Reducing the level and duration of exposure
- Provision of personal protective equipment, such as:
  - Face masks
  - Respirators
  - Protective clothing
  - Gloves

The latter must only be used as a last resort and never as a replacement for other control measures.

When determining these precautions it is important that you seek the views of other members of staff. In the last part of the assessment give details of procedures to be undertaken in the case of an emergency, for example, how to deal with a spillage. In the disposal column give details of how the substances are to be disposed of at the end of the experiment or after use. Finally list the supplier, so that the website can be located to look up further details.

Step 4: Ensure that control measures are used and maintained

Step 5: Information, training and supervision

Once the assessment has been completed it is important that employees are notified of the findings. They should be informed of:

- The substances they work with or could be exposed to
- The risks created by such exposure
- How to get access to the material safety data sheets that apply to those substances
- The main findings of the risk assessments
- The precautions that they should take to protect themselves and other employees
- How to use personal protective equipment and clothing provided
- What emergency procedures need to be followed

Staff should, where necessary, be trained in the control measures

6.12 Transport of microbiological cultures

There are legal requirements for the transport of cultures since they are regarded as an infectious substance. Most laboratories will be sending cultures for diagnostic purposes (e.g. further analysis of suspected *Salmonella* and *Listeria* isolates).

There are 4 steps required for the safe transport of microorganisms:

- Classification
- Packaging
- Labelling
- Transporting

Microorganisms can be divided into 2 categories. The list below has been modified for food microbiology laboratories since the regulations include microorganisms that would not be expected to be encountered in food microbiology laboratories, such as polio virus.

- Classification

Category A includes all hazard group 4 microorganisms, many hazard group 3 microorganisms and a few hazard group 2 microorganisms. Verotoxigenic strains of *E. coli* (hazard group 3) and *Clostridium botulinum* (hazard group 2) are category A. These are assigned to UN2814. They must be packed using packing instruction 620 (PI620). However, if transported by air, they require packaging instruction 602 (PI602).

Category B includes hazard group 1 and hazard group 2 microorganisms (with the exception of *Clostridium botulinum*) transported for diagnostic purposes. They are assigned to UN3373 and are packaged using packaging instruction 650 (PI650) for both terrestrial and air transport.

- Packaging

The packaging instructions and requirements are detailed in Tables A3 and A4 in the Appendix of the Advisory Committee on Dangerous Pathogens document Biological agents: Managing the risks in laboratories and healthcare premises. This document is freely available at www.hse.gov.uk/*biosafety/biologagents.pdf*

Table A3: Packaging Instruction 620

PACKING INSTRUCTION PI620

This instruction applies to UN 2814 and UN 2900.
The following packagings are authorised provided the special packing provisions are met (see below).
Packaging should be UN-type approved and consist of:
(a)   Inner packagings comprising:
   (i)   Leakproof primary receptacle(s)
   (ii)   A leakproof secondary packaging
   (iii)   Other than for solid infectious substances, an absorbent material in sufficient quantity to absorb the entire contents placed between the primary receptacle(s) and the secondary packaging; if multiple fragile primary receptacles are placed in a single secondary packaging, they shall be either individually wrapped or separated so as to prevent contact between them.
(b)   A rigid outer packaging of adequate strength for its capacity, mass and intended use. The smallest external dimension shall be not less than 100 mm.

Additional requirements:

1)   Inner packagings containing infectious substances shall not be consolidated with inner packagings containing unrelated types of goods. Complete packages may be overpacked; such an overpack may contain dry ice.
2)   Other than for exceptional consignments, e.g. whole organs which require special packaging, the following additional requirements shall apply:
   (a)   **Substances consigned at ambient temperatures or at a higher temperature.** Primary receptacles shall be of glass, metal or plastics. Positive means of ensuring a leakproof seal shall be provided, e.g. a heat seal, a skirted stopper or a metal crimp seal. If screw caps are used, they shall be secured by positive means, e.g. tape, paraffin sealing tape or manufactured locking closure.
   (b)   **Substances consigned refrigerated or frozen.** Ice, dry ice or other refrigerant shall be placed around the secondary packaging(s) or alternatively in an overpack with one or more complete packages marked in accordance with regulatory requirements. Interior supports shall be provided to secure secondary packaging(s) or packages in position after the ice or dry ice has dissipated. If ice is used, the outer packaging or overpack shall be leakproof. If dry ice is used, the outer packaging or overpack shall permit the release of carbon dioxide gas. The primary receptacle and the secondary packaging shall maintain their integrity at the temperature of the refrigerant used.
   (c)   **Substances consigned in liquid nitrogen.** Plastic primary receptacles capable of withstanding very low temperature shall be used. The secondary packaging shall also be capable of withstanding very low temperatures, and in most cases will need to be fitted over the primary receptacle individually. Provisions for the consignment of liquid nitrogen shall also be fulfilled. The primary receptacle and the secondary packaging shall maintain their integrity at the temperature of the liquid nitrogen.
   (d)   **Lyophilized substances.** May also be transported in primary receptacles that are flame-sealed glass ampoules or rubber-stoppered glass vials fitted with metal seals.
3)   Whatever the intended temperature of the consignment, the primary receptacle or the secondary packaging shall be capable of withstanding without leakage an internal pressure producing a pressure differential of not less than 95 kPa and temperatures in the range -40 °C to +55 °C.

Special packing provisions for infectious substances (Division 6.2)

Consignors of infectious substances shall ensure that packages are prepared in such a manner that they arrive at their destination in good condition and present no hazard to persons or animals during transport.

Liquids shall be filled into packagings, including IBCs, which have an appropriate resistance to the internal pressure that may develop under normal conditions of transport.

For UN 2814 and 2900, an itemised list of contents shall be enclosed between the secondary packaging and the outer packaging. When the infectious substances to be transported are unknown, but suspected of meeting the criteria for inclusion in Category A and assignment to UN 2814 or UN 2900, the words "suspected Category A infectious substance" shall be shown, in parentheses, following the proper shipping name on the document inside the outer packaging.

Before an empty packaging is returned to the consignor, or sent elsewhere, it shall be thoroughly disinfected or sterilized and any label or marking indicating that it had contained an infectious substance shall be removed or obliterated.

Note: The information given in Table A3 is based on the United Nations' Model Regulations on the Transport of Dangerous Goods 76.

Table A4: Packaging Instruction 650

PACKAGING INSTRUCTION PI650

This packing instruction applies to UN 3373.
1) The packaging shall be of good quality, strong enough to withstand the shocks and loadings normally encountered during carriage, including trans-shipment between vehicles and containers and between vehicles or containers and warehouses as well as any removal from a pallet or overpack for subsequent manual or mechanical handling. Packagings shall be constructed and closed to prevent any loss of contents that might be caused under normal conditions of carriage by vibration or by changes in temperature, humidity or pressure.
2) The packaging shall consist of three components:
    (a) A primary receptacle
    (b) A secondary packaging
    (c) An outer packaging
3) Primary receptacles shall be packed in secondary packagings in such a way that, under normal conditions of transport, they cannot break, be punctured or leak their contents into the secondary packaging. Secondary packagings shall be secured in outer packagings with suitable cushioning material. Any leakage of the contents shall not compromise the integrity of the cushioning material or of the outer packaging.
4) For transport, the mark illustrated in Figure 5 shall be displayed on the external surface of the outer packaging on a background of a contrasting colour and shall be clearly visible and legible. The width of the line shall be at least 2 mm; the letters and numbers shall be at least 6 mm high.
5) The completed package shall be capable of successfully passing the drop test set out in the regulations except that the height of the drop test shall not be less than 1.2 m. The smallest external dimension of the outer packagings shall not be less than 100 mm.
    Note: The information given in Table A3 is based on the United Nations' Model Regulations on the Transport of Dangerous Goods 76.

Figure 5: Packaging marking

6) For liquid substances:
   (a) The primary receptacle(s) shall be leakproof.
   (b) The secondary packaging shall be leakproof.
   (c) If multiple fragile primary receptacles are placed in a single secondary packaging, they shall be either individually wrapped or separated to prevent contact between them.
   (d) Absorbent material shall be placed between the primary receptacle(s) and the secondary packaging. The absorbent material shall be in quantity sufficient to absorb the entire contents of the primary receptacle(s) so that any release of the liquid substances will not compromise the integrity of the cushioning material or of the outer packaging.
   (e) The primary receptacle or the secondary packaging shall be capable of withstanding, without leakage, an internal pressure of 95 kPa (0.95 bar).

7) For solid substances:
   (a) The primary receptacle(s) shall be siftproof.
   (b) The secondary packaging shall be siftproof.
   (c) If multiple fragile primary receptacles are placed in a single secondary packaging, they shall be either individually wrapped or separated to prevent contact between them.

8) Refrigerated or frozen specimens: Ice, dry ice and liquid nitrogen:
   (a) When dry ice or liquid nitrogen is used to keep specimens cold, all applicable requirements of these Regulations shall be met. When used, ice or dry ice shall be placed outside the secondary packagings or in the outside packaging or an overpack. Interior supports shall be provided to secure the secondary packagings in the original position after the ice or dry ice has dissipated. If ice is used, the outside packaging or overpack shall be leakproof. If carbon dioxide, solid (dry ice) is used, the packaging shall be designed and constructed to permit the release of carbon dioxide gas to prevent a build-up pressure that could rupture the packagings and shall be marked "Carbon dioxide, solid" or "Dry ice".
   (b) The primary receptacle and the secondary packaging shall maintain their integrity at the temperature of the refrigerant used as well as the temperatures and the pressures that could result if refrigeration were lost.

9) Infectious substances assigned to UN 3373 and are packed and marked in accordance with this packing instruction are not subject to any other requirement in these Regulations.

10) Clear instructions on filling and closing such packages shall be provided by packaging manufacturers and subsequent distributors to the consignor or to the person who prepares the package (e.g. patient) to enable the package to be correctly prepared for transport.

11) If any substances has leaked or has been spilt in a vehicle or container, it may not be reused until after it has been thoroughly cleaned, and, if necessary disinfected or decontaminated. Any other goods or articles carried in the same vehicle or container shall be examined for possible contamination.

With source acknowledged.

Additional information on packaging of isolates for transport is also available in Annexes 3-4 of the IATA guidance document on the transport of infectious substances available at *www.iata.org/NR/rdonlyres/9C7E382B.../Guidance_Doc62DGR_51.pdf.*

- Labelling

Hazard group 2 strains will be classified as category B substance and are assigned to UN3373. Couriers may have their own specific requirements for the transport of cultures and they should be consulted prior to packaging cultures for transport.

- Other considerations

It is recommended that a record of details of all the cultures sent to other organisations/ laboratories is maintained.

References:
Anon. Biological agents: managing risks in laboratories and health care premises HSE
www.hse.gov.uk/biosafety/biologagents.pdf
Carriage of dangerous goods and use of transportable pressure equipment regulations 2004 authorisation No7.
www.hse.gov.uk/cdg/authorisations/auth07.pdf

6.13 Emergency procedures

All emergency procedures, such as fire drills, must be clearly documented and trained out, with all key personnel identified and maintained within their roles

The following procedures require documentation:

- Accident/first aid procedures and record book

- Emergency decontamination

- Fire action and evacuation

- RIDDOR (see Section 2.2.5)

- Isolation points for services e.g. gas/water

- Crisis/incident management procedure

7.   PORTABLE/TEMPORARY BUILDINGS

There are a wide variety of systems available and it is important to select a design that is well constructed and easy to clean. Wherever possible, the recommendations in the previous sections will apply but additional points listed below should be considered.

- Portable or temporary buildings require local authority permission for siting and should also be approved by the local fire prevention officer for the intended use.

- Care should be taken to ensure adequate foundations to prevent subsidence and sufficient anchorage to prevent wind movement in exposed locations.

- It would be prudent to choose a structure which meets BS476 'Fire tests on building materials and structures', since microbiology procedures often involve the use of Bunsen burners.

- The building itself should be sufficiently well insulated to prevent large temperature fluctuations. Portable buildings are often too cold in winter and too hot in summer. Sufficient heating and air conditioning for all season use will be required.

- Electrical connections should comply with the IEE Wiring Regulations (BS 7671) and adequate protection for incoming cables will be required. Ensure that the electrical system and water pipes are properly earthed.

- Water supply pipes and drainage will require protection from frost damage.

- Laboratory furniture will not normally be fixed to the walls in a portable or temporary structure. It is advisable to choose benching that can be cleaned beneath. Ensure that metal bench frames are earthed.

- Service access holes should be sealed to prevent entry of insects and rodents.

- Condensation may be a problem in some structures. Steam from autoclaves, steamers, water baths and media preparation will require extraction to prevent condensation on window frames, walls etc. Plastic cladding may attract dust, particularly in media preparation areas, and create cleaning problems.

8. REFURBISHING/EXTENDING AN EXISTING LABORATORY

The refurbishment and/or extension of an existing laboratory may involve aspects of one or more of the main activities that this document addresses as defined in the scope and objectives, *viz.*: a new build; reviewing and updating existing facilities; moving to a new facility and decommissioning an existing facility. Therefore, much of this guideline document will be relevant depending on the details of the planned laboratory refurbishment work during building operations. Important points to consider are measures required to avoid contamination of ongoing work, and health and safety implications for both staff and contractors.

There is likely to be advance warning for most major building work and as such there is time to plan accordingly. However, it is advisable to have a contingency plan to minimise laboratory disruption resulting from the need for emergency repairs of renovation following, for example, equipment malfunctioning, loss of services or accidental damage to the building.

8.1 Planned building work

8.1.1 Prior to building work

One of the most important aspects to consider is the scale of planned building work as this will have an impact on which options are available and most suitable in order to maintain laboratory work during such activity. For example, a decision may be made as to whether to close the whole laboratory, or segregate sections/rooms within the laboratory or an area within a room. Linked to this is the scheduling of the building work and the feasibility of phasing it to minimise disruption, which is easier if the laboratory operates over two or more levels, or a series of separate rooms, because isolation of specific areas can be more effectively achieved.

Where possible, the building work should be planned so as to minimise disruption to practical work (e.g. outside laboratory operating hours). Identifying the anticipated timing and duration of the building work can help to gauge how much disruption to practical work there will be and can help in assessing and deciding on laboratory management options. This may include considering the extent to which it is feasible to maintain the laboratory operating during the building work. If it is deemed feasible to keep it operating, then further consideration of whether segregation of areas of the laboratory is required and the extent to which the volume of work could be reduced may need to be considered. If continuation of laboratory work is not considered feasible, then options for sub-contracting the work or moving part, or all, of the laboratory functions into temporary (e.g. "PortaKabin"-style) facilities could be reviewed. When transporting laboratory equipment consideration should be given to the use of a removal company with proven experience in the transportation of laboratory equipment and that insurance liability is covered, particularly when delicate and expensive pieces of equipment are involved.

In order to manage and reduce the associated risks, a risk assessment should be carried out, the scope of which should include prevention of contamination of any ongoing laboratory work and the health and safety of both laboratory staff and building work contractors. Considerations for this risk assessment could include:

- Increase in noise levels

- Increase in vibration, particularly the effect on delicate instruments

- Changes in temperature and how this could affect personnel and laboratory instrumentation

- Dust levels, particularly the effect on HEPA filters and air conditioning ducts (which it may be necessary to protect)

- The impact that segregating areas will have on fire escape routes, and services (e.g. water and gas supply, access via false ceilings)

The output of this risk assessment should be the identification of activities that need to be carried out and risk management options and risk reduction measures that need to be implemented. These could include:

- Assigning a primary contact within the laboratory-based team (to liaise with the Project Manager etc.)

- Ensuring that all laboratory staff are aware of the proposed works to be carried out and timescales

- Defining 'out of bounds' areas for contractors and staff

- Agreeing and arranging access to the laboratory for contractors

- Providing appropriate safety training to contractors (e.g. awareness of microbiological hazards, 'out of bounds' areas, emergency escape routes)

- Organising relevant work permits for working in specific areas and working with specific equipment (e.g. gas cylinders)

- Decommissioning of equipment and, if required, preparation for transportation

- Decontaminating laboratory areas prior to contractors starting work and, if required, provision of a decontamination certificate

- Ensuring that there are sufficient laboratory environment QA/QC data (e.g. air sampling) to provide a benchmark of acceptable levels of contamination against which the post-building work levels can be assessed

8.1.2 During building work

During building work the following risk reduction measures and risk management options could be considered.

- Ensure that good communications are maintained, particularly if there are any problems or changes in agreed plans etc.

- If available (and feasible), perform as much laboratory work as possible in laminar air-flow cabinets and/or safety cabinets to minimise the possibility of contamination

- Increase cleaning programme in key areas (especially if dust is generated by the building work) and immediately prior to starting laboratory work

- Increase the frequency and numbers of QA/QC checks (e.g. sterility checks on media)

- Increase the frequency and sites of laboratory environment sampling (e.g. air sampling and settle plates)

8.1.3 After completion of building work

After completion of building work, the following should be done:

- Ensure that all snagging issues are dealt with as soon as possible

- Make arrangements for any services that may have been turned off during the building work to be turned on or reconnected

- Clean and decontaminate the area and verify its effectiveness by comparing subsequent laboratory environment QA/QC data with the acceptable levels established prior to the building work

- Clean and decontaminate any temporary (e.g. "PortaKabin"-style) facilities that were used

- If required, re-commission, re-calibrate and re-validate any equipment (e.g. balances) that were moved during the building work and verify that they are operating to the required specifications

- During the first few weeks following verification of successful re-commissioning and decontamination, an increased frequency of routine air monitoring and media sterility checks may be advisable to ensure that the area is not a source of sporadic and/or low level contamination

9.   DECOMMISSIONING A MICROBIOLOGY LABORATORY

Laboratory decommissioning requires careful planning to ensure that all safety issues are addressed during the process. This will involve a number of steps including:

Decontamination of the laboratory and equipment:

Moving and/or disposing of equipment, consumables, chemicals, organisms and samples.

Disconnection of services such as water and electricity.

It is likely that some items of protective clothing and personal protective equipment (PPE) will be required for the safe handling of materials and equipment during this process.

9.1   Decontamination of the laboratory and equipment

There are two key factors which will dictate the decontamination and regime used for a laboratory. The first consideration is the previous containment level that the laboratory operated under. Laboratories operating to Category 3 containment have specific requirements for decontamination and guidelines are available below.

In addition to the former use of the laboratory, the future use of the decommissioned facility will also play a role in the decontamination process for Category 2 laboratories.

Category 3:   Requires fumigation of both the laboratory area and equipment. Seek expert help regarding fumigation of environment and equipment as there are specialised health and safety requirements. Third party consultancy is strongly recommended.

Category 2:   Fumigation is not normally required and in most cases disinfection of surfaces will be sufficient. A risk assessment of future use of the facility would give an indication as to whether fumigation is needed to remove mould and bacterial spores, e.g. if future use is as a kitchen.

9.1.1 Decontamination of equipment surfaces

Equipment (and laboratory) surfaces should be cleaned with an appropriate laboratory disinfectant. Care should be taken to consult the instruction manuals of equipment to ensure that the disinfectants used are compatible with the equipment.

Once the laboratory and the equipment have been decontaminated it can then be either moved to the new facility or disposed of in the appropriate way.

9.2   Large equipment and services

When decommissioning a laboratory, there must be a logical and ordered schedule for the decommissioning and removal of equipment and services. Certain items of equipment and services will need to be left until final decommissioning, either because they will still be required or because removal of the equipment or associated services (ducting, pipe-work, cables etc.) will be disruptive to the environment/surroundings. The types of equipment/services which should be left until last include:

- Autoclave - for disposal of organisms and possible autoclaving of potentially contaminated equipment
- Glass washer
- Fume cupboard - due to opening of ducting being disrupted
- Disinfectant, cloths, buckets - for disinfection and cleaning.
- Large items - needing engineer help
- Services
  - Refrigeration
- Disconnection of water, gas, air handling etc.

9.3   Other items to consider

When decommissioning there will also be a number of additional items which will need to be transferred to a new laboratory or disposed of, including:

- Consumables
- Chemicals
- Glassware
- Organisms
- Samples
- Small items of equipment such as pipettors, mixers and hot plates

Many of these items do not have any specific safety requirements, although equipment and glassware that has been used for microbiological analysis will need to be disinfected/decontaminated before removal from the laboratory. Specific safety considerations need to be taken into account for the following:

9.3.1 Chemicals

All chemicals will need to be packed away for either moving to a new facility or disposal. The same rules for storage will apply and incompatible chemicals should be segregated as recommended by the supplier. Any hazardous chemicals should be disposed of via an authorised agent.

9.3.2 Organisms

Any organism to be disposed of should be autoclaved prior to disposal. If the cultures are to be relocated they should be packaged carefully to avoid possible damage during transit and labelled to indicate the contents of the container. The container should also have a label to show that it should only be opened in a laboratory. Cultures shipped by post or via a third party (e.g. courier or removal company) must be packaged and labelled in accordance with the regulations.

9.3.3 Samples

All samples should be autoclaved and/or discarded of in an appropriate manner.

9.4   Documentation

Manufacturers' equipment instructions should be retained with the associated equipment for future use, particularly if the equipment is being sold on.

Other records and results will need assessment with regard to their required retention time and then stored or disposed of appropriately.

Records of decommissioning activities, particularly as related to safety, should be kept. These could include the autoclave records for autoclaved contaminated items or cultures and service records for the decommissioning of equipment.

10. MOVING TO A NEW FACILITY

Many of the issues addressed in this document will apply to moving an existing laboratory to a new facility. The relevant Sections include: laboratory design/process flow, installation of equipment, and decommissioning an existing laboratory. Much of this guideline document will be relevant depending on the details of the planned laboratory move and consideration should be given to the health and safety implications for both staff and contractors (removal contactors as well as equipment and service engineers). **Details of the steps needed for decommissioning and decontamination are given in Section 9.**

11. REFERENCES

General reading

Lees, R. (1993). Design, construction and refurbishment of laboratories. Volume 2. Ellis Horwood, Chichester, ISBN 013034463X or ISBN 978013034463X.

Lees, R. and Smith, A.F. (1984). Design, construction and refurbishment of laboratories. Ellis Horwood, Chichester, ISBN 0853126453 or ISBN 9780853126454.

Legislation

Legislation changes frequently. It is essential to confirm that legislation cited in this publication and current at the time of printing, is still in force before acting upon it.

Antiterrorism, Crime and Security Act (2001). Part 7 Security of Pathogens and Toxins. Office of Public Sector Information. Available online at *http://www.opsi.gov.uk/acts/acts2001/ukpga_20010024_en_6#pt7*

The Building Regulations 2000 (SI 2000/2530). The Stationery Office, Norwich

The Building (Approved Inspectors etc.) Regulations 2000 (SI 2000/2532). The Stationery Office, Norwich

The Building and Approved Inspectors (Amendment No.2) Regulations 2009 (SI 2009/2465). The Stationery Office, Norwich

The Building (Amendment No.2) Regulations 2009 (SI 2009/2397). The Stationery Office, Norwich.

The Building and Approved Inspectors (Amendment) Regulations 2009 (SI 2009/1219). The Stationery Office, Norwich

The Building (Amendment) Regulations 2009 (SI 2009/466). The Stationery Office, Norwich

Collection and Disposal of Waste Regulations. SI 1988 no. 819, ISBN 9780110868196. The Stationery Office, Norwich

The Construction (Design and Management) Regulations 2007 (CDM 2007 SI 2007 No 320) available online at http://www.opsi.gov.uk/si/si2007/pdf/uksi_20070320_en.pdf

The Control of Asbestos at Work Regulations. SI 2002 no. 2675, ISBN 0110429184. The Stationery Office, Norwich

Control of Noise at Work Regulations. SI 2005 no. 1643 ISBN 9780110729848. The Stationery Office, Norwich

Control of Substances Hazardous to Health (COSHH) Regulations, SI 2002 no. 2677,ISBN 0110429192. The Stationery Office, Norwich

Dangerous Substances and Explosive Atmospheres Regulations SI 2002/2776. The Stationery Office, Norwich

The Diseases of Animals (Approved Disinfectants) (England) Order. SI 2007 no. 448. ISBN 9780110758282. The Stationery Office, Norwich

EC Council Directive 90/679/EEC. Protection of workers from risks related to exposure to biological agents at work. Available online at *http://www.biosafety.be/GB/Dir.Eur.GB/Other/90_679/TC.html*

Electricity at Work Regulations. SI 1989 no. 635, ISBN 978011096635. The Stationery Office, Norwich

Environmental Protection Act 1990. The Stationery Office, Norwich

Food Safety Act 1990. ISBN 9780105416906. The Stationery Office, Norwich

Gas Safety (Installation and Use) Regulations. SI 1998 no. 2451. ISBN 9780110796550. The Stationery Office, Norwich

Genetically Modified Organisms (Contained Use) Regulations, 2000 (SI 2000/2831). The Stationery Office, Norwich

Hazardous Waste (England and Wales) Regulations 2005 (SI 2005/894). The Stationery Office, Norwich

Health and Safety (Display Screen Equipment) Regulations. SI 1992 no. 2792. ISBN 9780110259192. The Stationery Office, Norwich

Health and Safety (First Aid) Regulations. SI 1981 no. 917. ISBN 9780110169170. The Stationery Office, Norwich

Health and Safety at Work Act 1974. ISBN 9780105437741. The Stationery Office, Norwich

The Highly Flammable Liquids Regulations (1974) HMSO.

The Highly Flammable Liquids and Liquified Petroleum Gases Regulations (1972) HMSO.

HSE (2000). Safety of pressure systems. Pressure systems safety regulations ISBN 978 0 11 085836 4. The Stationery Office, Norwich

IEE Wiring regulations webpages. Institution of Engineering and Technology. *http://www.theiet.org* (accessed 22/11/07).

Management of Health and Safety at Work Regulations. SI 1999 no. 3242, ISBN 9789999017848. The Stationery Office, Norwich

Manual Handling Operations Regulations. SI 1992 no.2 793. ISBN 9780110259208. The Stationery Office, Norwich

Manual to the Building Regulations (2001). The Stationery Office
- Approved document Part A Structure (2006)
- Approved document Part C Site preparation and resistance to contaminants and moisture (2006)
- Approved document Part D Toxic substances (2006)
- Approved document Part E Resistance to the passage of sound (2006)
- Approved document Part F Ventilation (2006)
- Approved document Part G Hygiene (2006)
- Approved document Part H Drainage and waste disposal (2006)
- Approved document Part J Combustion appliances and fuel storage systems (2006)
- Approved document Part K Protection from falling, collision and impact (2006)
- Approved document Part L2A Conservation of fuel and power. New buildings other than dwellings (2006)
- Approved document Part L2B Conservation of fuel and power. Existing buildings other than dwellings (2006)
- Approved document Part M Access and use of buildings (2006)
- Approved document Part N Glazing, safety in relation to impact, opening and cleaning (2006)

Methylated Spirits Regulations. SI 1987 no. 2009 ISBN 9780110780092. The Stationery Office, Norwich

Offices, Shops and Railway Premises Act 1963. ISBN 9780108501111. The Stationery Office, Norwich

Personal Protective Equipment at Work Regulations. SI 1992 no. 2966. ISBN 9780110258324. The Stationery Office, Norwich

Plugs and Sockets etc. (Safety) Regulations. SI 1994 no. 1768, ISBN 9780110447681. The Stationery Office, Norwich

The Poultry Breeding Flocks and Hatcheries (England) Order. SI 2007 no. 405. ISBN 9780110758190. The Stationery Office, Norwich

Pressure Systems and Transportable Gas Containers Regulations, SI 1989 no. 2169, ISBN 0110981693. The Stationery Office, Norwich

Provision and Use of Work Equipment Regulations. SI 1992 no. 2932. ISBN 9780110258492. The Stationery Office, Norwich

Radioactive Substances Act (1993). Available online at (*http://www.hmso.gov.uk/acts/acts1993/Ukpga_19930012_en_1_htm*).

The Regulatory Reform (Fire Safety) Order 2005 (SI 2005 No 1541). The Stationery Office, Norwich

Reporting of Injuries, Diseases and Dangerous Occurrences Regulations (RIDDOR 1995). Available online at (*http://www.hse.gov.uk/riddor*).

Schedule 5. Statutory Instrument 929 (2007) Prevention and Suppression of Terrorism. The Schedule 5 to the Anti-terrorism, Crime and Security Act 2001 (Modification) Order 2007. Office of Public Sector Information Available online at *http://www.opsi.gov.uk/si/si2007/uksi_20070929_en_1.*

The Waste Management (England and Wales) Regulations 2006 SI 2006/937. The Stationery Office, Norwich

Water Supply (Water Fittings) Regulations 1999 SI 1999/1148. The Stationery Office, Norwich

Workplace (Health, Safety and Welfare) Regulations. SI 1992 no. 3004, ISBN 9780110340494 *http://www.hse.gov.uk/pubns/priced/l24.pdf* NB: (partially revoked by Dangerous Substances and Explosive Atmospheres Regulations SI 2002 no. 2776).

Standards

BS 470 (1984). Specification for inspection, access and entry openings for pressure vessels, ISBN 0580134520. Available online at *http://www.hse.gov.uk/foi/internalops/fod/oc/300-399/307_7.pdf*

BS 476 (various) Fire tests on building materials and structures BSI online

BS 1710 (1984 Confirmed 2007). Specification for identification of pipelines and services, ISBN 0 580 13859 3. BSI online

BS 2646 Autoclaves for sterilisation in laboratories.
* Part 1 (1993 Confirmed 2006). Specification for design, construction, safety and performance. ISBN 0 580 21336 6. BSI online
* Part 2 (1990 Confirmed 2006). Guide to planning and installation. ISBN 0 580 18995 3. BSI online
* Part 3 (1993 Confirmed 2006). Guide to safe use and operation. ISBN 0 580 225119. BSI online
* Part 4 (1991 Confirmed 2006). Guide to maintenance. ISBN 0 580 193489. BSI online
* Part 5 (1993 Confirmed 2006). Methods of test for function and performance. ISBN 0580021337 4. BSI online
* Biotechnology. Performance criteria for steam sterilisers and autoclaves. BS EN 12347:1998. BSI online

BS 2648 (1955 Confirmed 2006). Performance requirements for electrically heated laboratory drying ovens. ISBN 0580326659. BSI online

BS 3202 Laboratory Furniture and Fittings. BSI online
* Part 1 (1991 Confirmed 2007). Introduction. ISBN 0 580 19484 1.
* Part 2 (1991 Confirmed 1997). Specification for performance. ISBN 0 580 19485 X (partially replaced by BS EN 13150 (2001). Workbenches for laboratories. Dimensions, safety requirements and test methods. ISBN 0 580 37931 0.

BS 3970 Sterilizing and disinfecting equipment for medical products. BSI online
* Part 1 (1990 Confirmed 2006). Specification for general requirements. ISBN 0580 179400.
* Part 2 (1991 Confirmed 2006). Specification for steam sterilisers for aqueous fluids in sealed rigid containers. ISBN 058019797 2.
* Part 5 (1990 Confirmed 2006). Specification for low temperature steam disinfectors. ISBN 0580185087.

BS 5726 (2005). Microbiological Safety Cabinets. Information to be supplied by the purchaser to the vendor and to the installer and siting and use of cabinets. Recommendations and guidance, ISBN 0580455904. BSI online

BS 5925 (1991 Confirmed 2007). Code of practice for ventilation principles and designing for natural ventilation. ISBN 0 580 19285 7. BSI online

BS 6700 (2006). Design, installation, testing and maintenance of services supplying water for domestic use within buildings and their curtiliages. Specification. ISBN 0 580 49786 0. BSI online

BS 7671 IEE Wiring regulations and adequate protection for incoming cables. BSI online

BS EN 285 (1997). Sterilization. Steam sterilizers. Large sterilizers ISBN 058027635x (current but revised by BS EN 285 (2006)). Sterilization. Steam sterilizers. Large sterilizers. ISBN 0580 486885. BSI online

BS EN 837 part 1 (1998). Pressure gauges. Bourdon tube pressure gauges. Dimensions, metrology, requirements and testing, ISBN 058 288935. BSI online

BS EN 12457:1999+A1 2009 Centrifuges: Common safety requirements ISBN 9780580620416. BSI online

BS EN 12469: 2000 Biotechnology. Performance criteria for microbiology safety cabinets ISBN: 0580348695. BSI online

BS EN 12778 (2002). Cookware. Pressure cookers for domestic use. ISBN 058040904X. BSI online

BS EN 13060 (2004). Small steam sterilizers. ISBN 0580461874. BSI online

BS EN 14056 (2003) Laboratory furniture. Recommendations for design and installation. ISBN 0 580 41558 9. BSI online

BS EN 14175-6 Fume Cupboards. BSI online
- Part 1 (2003) Vocabulary, ISBN 0 580 429474.
- Part 2 (2003) Safety and performance requirements, ISBN 0580429466.
- Part 3 (2007) Type test methods, ISBN 978 0 580 50371 9.
- Part 4 (2007) On-site test methods, ISBN 978 0580 50372 6.
- Part 6 (2007) Variable air volume fume cupboards, ISBN 978 0 580 50374 0.

DD CEN/TS 14175 part 5 (2006) Fume cupboards. Recommendations for installation and maintenance, ISBN 978 0 580 50373 3. BSI online

Codes of practice/advice documents

A guide for new and expectant mothers who work. INDG373. Available online at (*http://hse.gov.uk/pubns/indg373.pdf*).

A guide to risk assessment requirements: Common provisions in health and safety law. Leaflet INDG218, HSE Books 1996 (single copy free or priced packs of 5
ISBN 0 7176 1211 2) or available online at: *http://www.hse.gov.uk/pubns/INDG218.pdf*

A short guide to making your premises safe from fire
http://www.communities.gov.uk/documents/fire/pdf/144647.pdf

Advisory Committee on Dangerous Pathogens (ACDP) Approved List of Biological Agents
www.hse.gov.uk/pubns/misc208.pdf

Advisory Committee on Dangerous Pathogens (2003) Infection at work: Controlling the risks. Available as a download *http://www.hse.gov.uk/pubns/infection.pdf*

Advisory Committee on Dangerous Pathogens: Infection risks to new and expectant mothers in the workplace, a guide for employers *http://www.hse.gov.uk/pubns/infection.pdf*

Advisory Committee on Dangerous Pathogens (2001) The management, design and operation of microbiological containment laboratories. Health and Safety Executive, ISBN 0717620344.

Approved Code of Practice on Dangerous Substances and Explosive Atmospheres
http://www.hse.gov.uk/pubns/priced/l138.pdf

Approved Code of Practice on Managing Health and Safety in Construction
http://www.hse.gov.uk/pubns/priced/l144.pdf

Approved Code of Practice on Safety of Transportable Gas Containers. HMSO, ISBN 011 88555 158.

Approved Code of Practice on Storage of Dangerous Substances. Available online at
http://www.hse.gov.uk/pubns/priced/l135.pdf

Approved Code of Practice: The Management of Asbestos in Non-Domestic Premises, L127,
ISBN 9780 7176 6209 8 (2006). HSE Books

Betts, R.P., Oscroft, C.A. and Baylis, C.L. (eds.) (2004) A Code of Practice for Microbiology Laboratories Handling Food, Drink and Associated Samples. Guideline 9. Campden BRI

Biological Agents: Managing the Risks in the Laboratory and Healthcare Premises: Available online at
http://www.hse.gov.uk/biosafety/biologagents.pdf

BOC Handbook 'Safety in the use of compressed gas cylinders'. Available online at
(*http://www.boc.com/index.asp*)

Carriage of dangerous goods and use of transportable pressure equipment regulations 2004 authorisation No. 7. Available online at *http://www.hse.gov.uk/cdg/authorisations/auth07.pdf*

CIBSE (2002) Minimising the risk of Legionnaire's disease (TM13) Chartered Institution of Building Services Engineers ISBN 1903287235.

Committee on Hazardous Biological Substances in the Laboratory, National Research Council (1989). Biosafety in the laboratory. National Academy Press, Washington D.C. ISBN 0 309 03975 4 or ISBN 978 0309039758

Customs and Excise (Notice 473) Production, distribution and use of denatured alcohol. HMRC 2010

Department of Health (2006) Health Technical Memorandum 07-01: Safe Management of Healthcare Waste. Available as a download *http://www.dh.gov.uk/dr_consum_dh/groups/dh_digitalassets/documents/digitalasset/dh_073328.pdf*

Department of Health (2006) Safe management of healthcare waste. The Stationery Office. ISBN 9780113227662.

Department of the Environment (1983) Clinical wastes: a technical memorandum on arisings, treatment and disposal including a code of practice. Waste Management Paper no.25. HMSO ISBN 0117517194.

Five steps to risk assessment Leaflet INDG163(rev1) HSE Books 1998 (single copy free or priced packs of 10 ISBN 0 7176 1565 0) or available online at: *www.hse.gov.uk/pubns/INDG163.pdf*

Health and Safety Regulations - A short guide. Available online at *http://www.hse.gov.uk/pubns/hsc13.pdf*

Health Services Advisory Committee (2003) Safe working and the prevention of infection in clinical laboratories and similar facilities (2nd edition). Health and Safety Executive. ISBN 0717625133.

Health Service Advisory Committee (2003) Safe Working and the Prevention of Infection in the Mortuary and Post Mortem Room. 2nd edition. Health and Safety Executive, ISBN 0717622932.

Home Office/The Scottish Office. Fire Precautions Act 1971, Fire Safety at Work (1991) HMSO ISBN 0 11 340905 2.

HSE (2007) Memorandum of guidance on the electricity at work regulations 1989. Guidance on regulations, 2nd edition. Health and Safety Executive. ISBN 978 0 717662289.

HSE (2005) Controlling noise at work. The control of noise at work regulations 2005. Guidance on regulations (2nd edition). Health and Safety Executive, ISBN 0717661644.

HSE (2005) HSG56 Noise guides 3 to 8: Noise assessment, information and control. ISBN 011885 430

HSE (2004) Maintaining portable and transportable electrical apparatus. Health and Safety Executive, ISBN 0717628051.

HSE (2003) Safe working and the prevention of infection in clinical laboratories and similar facilities. 2nd edition. Health and Safety Executive. Health Services Advisory Committee. ISBN 0717625133.

HSE (2003) Work with display screen equipment: Health and safety (display screen equipment) regulations 1992 as amended by the Health and safety (miscellaneous amendment) regulations 2002. Guidance on regulations. Health and Safety Executive, ISBN 0717625826.

HSE (2001) Legionnaires disease. The control of legionella bacteria in water systems. Approved code of practice and guidance systems, 3rd edition. Health and Safety Executive, ISBN 0717617726.

HSE (2000) Common Zoonoses in Agriculture. Available as a download
http://www.hse.gov.uk/pubns/ais2.pdf

HSE (2000) General ventilation in the workplace. Guidance for employers. Health and Safety Executive, ISBN 9780717617937.

HSE (2000) Safety of pressure systems. Pressure systems safety regulations 2000. Approved code of practice. Health and Safety Executive. ISBN 071761767X.

HSE (1998) Compressed air safety (2nd edition). Health and Safety Executive, ISBN 0717615316.

HSE (1998) Lighting at Work HS(G)38, 2nd edition. Health and Safety Executive, ISBN 0717612325

HSE (1998) Seating at Work HS(G)57, 3rd edition. Health and Safety Executive, ISBN 978071761231.

HSE (1997) First aid at work. The health and safety (first aid) regulations 1981. Approved code of practice and guidance. Health and Safety Executive, ISBN 0717610500.

HSE (1991) The control of legionellosis, including legionnaires' disease HS(G)70 HSMO 1991
ISBN 0 11 885660 X

HSE (1990) Guidance Note PM 73 Safety at Autoclaves. HMSO.

HSE (1990) Ventilation. Respiratory protective equipment: A practical guide for users. HSE Books 1990 ISBN 0 11 885522.

HSE (1989) A guide to the electricity at work regulations 1989. An open learning course. Health and Safety Executive/HMSO ISBN 0 11 885443 7.

HSE (1989) Guide to Pressure Systems and Transportable Gas Containers Regulations. Health and Safety Executive OC 308/13.

HSE website: *http://www.hse.gov.uk/forms/notification/cba1notes.htm.*

IATA guidance document on the transport of infectious substances available at *www.iata.org/NR/rdonlyres/9C7E382B.../Guidance_Doc62DGR_51.pdf.*

Infection at work: controlling the risks Advisory Committee on Dangerous Pathogens 2003 available online at: *http:// www.hse.gov.uk/pubns/infection.pdf*

Infection Risks to New and Expectant Mothers in the Workplace: A guide for Employers (HSE Books ISBN 9780717613601)

New and expectant mother at work, a guide for employers HS(G)122

NHS Estates (2005) Facilities for mortuary and post mortem rooms. Health Building Note 20. 3rd edition. Department of Health, ISBN 0113227159

Sykes, J.M. (1989) Sick building syndrome: A review (1989). Specialist inspector report No. 10. published by the HSE Technology Division

The Management, Design and Operation of Microbiological Containment: Laboratories: (HSE Books ISBN: 9780717620340).

The right start INDG364. Available online at *http://www.hse.gov.uk/pubns/indg364.pdf*

Young people at work; a guide for employers HSG165. HSE 2000. ISBN 0-7176-1889-7. Available online at *http://www.healthandsafetyworksni.gov.uk/employing_young_people_in_the_workplace_-_a_guide_for_employers-2.pdf*